BLAIRSVILLE SENIOR HIGH SCHOOL
BLAIRSVILLE. PENNA.

Math

FOR EVERYDAY LIVING

[adele Lorraine Ilijanich, editor]

513
MAT

Ideal Publications

A Division of Ideal School Supply Company

11000 South Lavergne Avenue
Oak Lawn, Illinois 60453

CREDITS

This text is based on the practical life skills unit of the Math Mastery Center, a comprehensive integrated teaching/learning system developed by Westinghouse Learning Corporation, utilizing mastery learning concepts and techniques.

The objective base, the instructional techniques, and the lessons were formulated by the Mastery Center development staff:

Program Designer: Douglas J. Paul, B.S., University of Wisconsin, M.A., University of Iowa.

Design Editor: Wayne Prophet, B.A., Northeastern University; M.A., A.B.D., University of Iowa.

Writers: Darlene Cornell, B.S., University of Wisconsin; Judith Lawson, B.A., M.A., Ph.D., University of Iowa; Timothy Lowe, B.A., University of Iowa; Thomas Paul, B.A., M.A., University of Wisconsin.

Dr. William Nibbelink, Professor of Mathematics Education at the University of Iowa, served as consultant in development of the objective base and instructional sequences for the Math Mastery Center.

Adele Lorraine Ilijanich served as editor for *Math for Everyday Living,* converting the multimedia content of the Mastery Center program into textbook format, and developing the Self-Tests at the end of each chapter. She holds B.S. and M.S. degrees from Indiana State University.

Eighth Printing
© 1980 Ideal Publications
11000 South Lavergne Avenue, Oak Lawn, IL 60453

All rights reserved. No part of this book may
be reproduced or transmitted in any form or
by any means, electronic or mechanical,
including photocopying and recording, or by
any information storage or retrieval system,
without permission in writing from
the publisher.

Printed in the U.S.A.
ISBN Number: 0-89099-508-7

AN IMPORTANT MESSAGE

Why should I learn all this math? What good will it ever do me?

These are questions which almost everyone has asked at one time, and *Math for Everyday Living* was written to *show* you why you should learn math and exactly what good it *will* do you in daily life experiences.

The fact is that in today's world, no one can function as an effective, independent person without the ability to perform a wide range of math operations. To make clear to you just what math you really need, we have developed a different kind of math book—one that presents math as it is used in a number of real life activities. For example, going shopping, or taking a trip, or having a job.

As in real life, most of the problems in this book will require that you do more than one math operation. For instance, you may have to convert a percent to a decimal, then multiply, then add, all in one problem.

ORGANIZATION OF THE BOOK

At the beginning of each chapter there is a list of "key words" which are vital to that chapter. Each chapter is divided into a series of skills which are related to the overall theme of the chapter. (For example, in Chapter 1, Going Shopping, the first skill is to find the sale price of an item when a discount is given.)

Before you get to the actual problems, however, there is a discussion of why you need to have this particular skill in the first place, then one or more sample problems, with each step in solving the problem carefully worked out.

Following the general explanation of the skill and the sample problems, there are usually two sets of problems. In the first set of problems, you will notice that the first one or two have check marks (√) beside them. The answers to these checked problems are in the last section of the book, beginning on page 306. We suggest that you first work the problems with the check marks, then see if you got the correct answer. If you did not, read the explanation and study the sample problem again, then redo the problem you missed. If you still do not have the correct answer, check with your teacher before going on to the rest of the problems.

The second set of problems for each skill is provided for extra practice.

(*Suggestion:* After working all the problems in the first set out, try using a hand calculator to solve the extra practice problems.)

You will find that all of the skills presented in *Math for Everyday Living* are practical ones, essential to existence in today's society. We have tried to present each skill in a way which you can not only clearly understand, but, also, hopefully enjoy.

Anja, Ranzo, and Miro welcome you to *Math for Everyday Living,* and wish you success.

CONTENTS

MIRO

ANJA

RANZO

INTRODUCTION: MEET THE ARITHMIANS

They are now on their way to Earth from their home in outer space. Their native planet was completely destroyed during a terrible war with a neighboring planet. These three Arithimians are the only survivors of the war, because they escaped in their spaceship just before the final explosion.

Now that they're on their way to Earth, they have a lot to learn. Although they know the basics of our life here, you will find through their adventures that they have trouble using what they know. Let's join them on their journey to Earth.

1

The Arithimians survived a terrible war on their own planet, but:
- Can they survive life in America?
- Can they adjust to their new life?
- Can they learn the math skills necessary to live in America?
- How will they learn to use the arithmetic skills they already have while shopping and working?
- Will they learn to figure taxes, discounts, and budgets?

Remember, the Arithmians know the basics, as you do. You will see that they have trouble applying what they know when they encounter everyday situations in America.

CHAPTER

GOING SHOPPING

**USING BASIC MATH SKILLS TO SOLVE PROBLEMS
RELATED TO SHOPPING.**

KEY WORDS:

1. **Discount:** the amount of money subtracted from the regular price when an item goes on sale.
2. **Percent:** one one-hundredth part; for example, 4 percent is 4 one-hundredths, or 4 parts out of 100.
3. **Estimate:** to make a guess at a total price without exact figuring.
4. **Subtotal:** sum of goods purchased before the tax is added.
5. **Sales Tax:** a small percentage of each dollar that is added to the total bill. The store must give this money to the state or local government.

SKILL: Find the sale price of an item when a discount is given, either as a percentage or a fraction of the price.

The Arithmians have safely landed in America. They are worried about looking so different from the Americans, and Anja calls a meeting to discuss her plan for buying clothes like the Americans wear. Ranzo volunteers to go out that night and find out what Americans wear. He reports that almost everyone is wearing blue jeans and T-shirts, so the next morning, the Arithmians go to a nearby store to buy some blue jeans and T-shirts.

The blue jeans cost	minus the 10% discount	what the Arithimians pay.
$9.80	- 10%	= ?

Original Cost	$9.80		Original Cost	$9.80
Discount	x .10		Amount of	
	.980 The amount of price decrease		Discount	- .98
				$8.82 Arithmians' price.

TO FIND DISCOUNT PRICE:

A.	B.	C.	D.
¼ of $2.20 = ¼ x $2.20	$\frac{1}{4} \times \frac{\$2.20}{1} = \frac{\$2.20}{4}$	$\begin{array}{r} .55 \\ 4\overline{)\,\$2.20} \\ 2\,0 \\ \overline{20} \\ 20 \\ \end{array}$	Original Price $2.20 Amount of Discount - .55 Arithmians Pay $1.65

SO: ¼ of $2.20 = .55 off the regular price.

    The Arithmians must do more shopping for items they will need for everyday living in America. The prices shown on the items below are the regular prices. See if you can figure the sale or discount price for each item. (Round the discount price to the nearest cent.)

SAMPLE:

A hammer, regularly $10.95, now 15% off.

Step 1: Multiply regular price times discount.

$$\begin{array}{r} \$ 10.95 \\ \times\ \ .15 \\ \hline 5475 \\ 1095 \\ \hline \$1.6425 = \$1.64 \end{array}$$

Step 2: Subtract your answer from the regular price.

$$\begin{array}{r} \$ 10.95 \\ -\ \ 1.64 \\ \hline \$\ \ 9.31 \end{array}$$

Discount Price = ___$9.31___

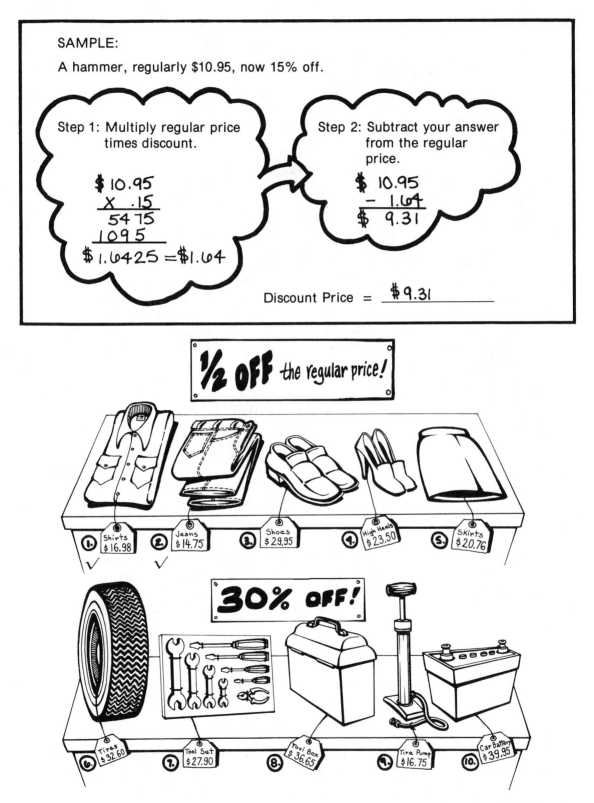

½ OFF the regular price!

1. Shirts $16.98
2. Jeans $14.75
3. Shoes $29.95
4. High Heels $23.50
5. Skirts $20.76

30% OFF!

6. Tires $32.60
7. Tool Set $27.90
8. Tool Box $36.65
9. Tire Pump $16.75
10. Car Battery $39.95

Here are some more items which Anja, Ranzo, and Miro found on sale. Figure the discount or sale price for these items. (Round the discount price to the nearest cent.)

1. An electric drill, regularly $17.67, on sale for 20% off.

2. A table, $89.95, now 1/3 off.

3. A television set, $99.95; 15% off.

4. An $11.98 shirt, 1/2 off.

5. A record player, regularly $55.20, now 1/4 off.

6. A $39.44 lamp, 10% off.

7. A footstool, usually $17.98, on sale for 1/3 off.

8. A $125.00 rocking chair, now 40% off.

9. A $105.09 camera, now 1/4 off.

10. A $22.50 sweater, 1/2 off.

11. A $78.80 radio, 30% off.

12. A $15.00 saw, now 25% off.

13. A warm parka, regularly $36.45, now 15% off.

14. A $499.79 tape recorder, now 1/3 off.

SKILL: Figure the cost of a fraction of an item.

The Arithmians must also go to the grocery store to buy food. Many of the items they find there are priced per pound. What happens, they wonder, if they only want a part of a pound? Ranzo, for example, found that apples are 87¢ per pound.

TO FIND THE PRICE OF A FRACTION OF AN ITEM:

A.	B.	C.
1/3 of $.87 = 1/3 x $.87	$\dfrac{1}{3} \times \dfrac{\$.87}{1} = \dfrac{\$.87}{3}$	$\begin{array}{r} \$\ .29 \quad \text{for 1/3 lb.} \\ 3\overline{)\ \$\ .87} \\ 6 \\ \overline{27} \\ 27 \\ \hline \end{array}$

A.	B.	C.
3/4 of $.48 = 3/4 x $.48	$\dfrac{3}{4} \times \dfrac{\$.48}{1} = \dfrac{\$1.44}{4}$	$\begin{array}{r} \$\ .36 \text{ for 3/4 lb.} \\ 4\overline{)\ \$1.44} \\ 1\ 2 \\ \overline{24} \\ 24 \\ \hline \end{array}$

Now, see if you can find the price for these items. (Round the problems to the nearest cent.)

√ 1. 1/3 lb. cantaloupe at $.88 a pound.   √ 2. 3/4 lb. onions at $.49 a pound.

3. 1/2 lb. hamburger at $1.89 per pound.

4. 3/4 lb. steak at $3.10 per pound.

5. 1/4 lb. turkey at $.69 per lb.

6. 1/2 lb. fish at $1.58 per lb.

7. 3/4 lb. cucumbers at 36¢ per lb.

8. 1/2 lb. watermelon at $.50 per lb.

9. 1/4 lb. peanuts at $1.10 per lb.

10. 3/4 lb. green beans at 48¢ per lb.

Here are some other grocery items the Arithmians saw. Figure the cost for each fraction of an item. Work your answers to the nearest cent.

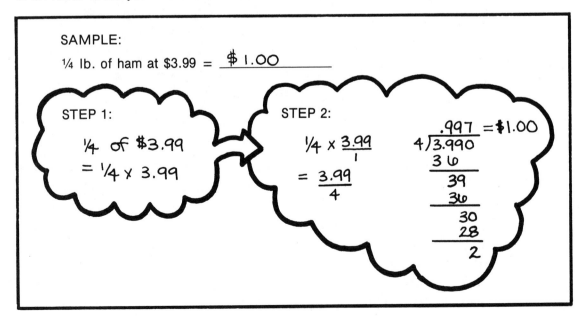

SAMPLE:

¼ lb. of ham at $3.99 = $ 1.00

STEP 1:

¼ of $3.99
= ¼ × 3.99

STEP 2:

¼ × $\frac{3.99}{1}$
= $\frac{3.99}{4}$

$$\begin{array}{r} .997 = \$1.00 \\ 4\overline{)3.990} \\ \underline{3\ 6} \\ 39 \\ \underline{36} \\ 30 \\ \underline{28} \\ 2 \end{array}$$

Going Shopping

1. 3/4 lb. of apples at $.32 lb.

2. 1/2 lb. of beans at $.42 lb.

3. 3/4 lb. of beef ribs at $2.65 lb.

4. 12 lbs. watermelon at $.39 lb.

5. 1/4 lb. of tomatoes at $.77 lb.

6. 1/2 lb. of oranges at $1.25 lb.

7. 1/4 sack of rice at $3.57 per sack.

8. 3/4 lb. of chicken at $.68 lb.

9. 1/2 lb. of pork chops at $2.25 lb.

10. 1/4 lb. of shrimp at $4.68 lb.

11. 3/4 lb. of onions at $.29 lb.

12. 1/2 lb. of sausage at $.94 lb.

13. 1/4 lb. of cheese at $1.63 lb.

14. 3/4 lb. of butter at $1.48 lb.

SKILL: Estimate the total cost of several items.

The Arithmians must be careful not to spend more money than they have. Anja knows how to estimate, but Ranzo and Miro do not.

WHY DID RANZO ROUND $3.10 To $3.50?

WHEN YOU'RE SHOPPING, YOU WANT TO MAKE SURE THAT WHEN YOU GET TO THE CHECK-OUT COUNTER, YOU DON'T HAVE MORE MERCHANDISE THAN MONEY. TO DO THAT, YOU SHOULD ROUND OFF TO THE NEXT 50 CENTS. ALWAYS GO UP!

Round each of the items listed below up to the next half dollar (50 cents) or dollar. Then add to get the total. (The first two prices have already been rounded for you.)

✓ 1.

Item	Price	Rounded
Notebook	$ 1.37	$1.50
Paper	.67	1.00
Pencils	1.15	
Shoes	18.63	
Shirt	13.47	
Scarf	3.86	
Wallet	4.25	
	TOTAL	

2.

Item	Price	Rounded
Radio	$17.88	
Purse	16.19	
Socks	1.33	
Iron	24.56	
Clock	7.46	
Thermos	12.50	
Sunglasses	4.93	
	TOTAL	

3.

Item	Price	Rounded
Deodorant	$ 1.29	
Shampoo	2.44	
Soap	.62	
Vitamins	4.12	
Toothpaste	.76	
Magazine	1.10	
Cat Food	1.81	
Floor Mop	3.35	
	TOTAL	

4.

Item	Price	Rounded
Bread	$ .75	
Cookies	1.19	
Milk	1.83	
Lettuce	.95	
Hamburger	1.64	
Soup	.24	
Crackers	.89	
Flour	3.09	
	TOTAL	

On each of these shopping lists, round each price to the next half dollar (50 cents) or dollar. Then add the rounded prices to get the total.

1.

Item	Price	Rounded
Pens	$ 1.38	
Ruler	.93	
Book	12.45	
Stamps	3.30	
Book Bag	15.27	
Calculator	27.53	
Bicycle Tire	6.66	
TOTAL		

2.

Item	Price	Rounded
Hat	$ 3.78	
Glue	1.12	
Eraser	.31	
Lunch Box	8.77	
Lamp	14.23	
Pillow	3.44	
Gym Shoes	12.61	
TOTAL		

3.

Item	Price	Rounded
Toothbrush	$ 1.02	
Hair Spray	1.70	
Mouthwash	.87	
Comb	.23	
Dog Food	3.72	
Sponge	.36	
Clothespins	1.75	
Hand Cream	2.34	
TOTAL		

4.

Item	Price	Rounded
Buns	$ .67	
Cake	2.34	
Cream	1.13	
Spinach	.82	
Ketchup	.76	
Pickles	1.45	
TV Dinner	1.29	
Coffee	5.51	
TOTAL		

If the Arithmians want to buy the following items and need to know the exact cost, how can they find that exact cost? (Use a 4% sales tax to figure these problems. However, the sales tax in your state may be different.)

Paper	$ .67	Thermos	$12.50
Hamburger	1.64	Bread	.75
Shampoo	2.44	Milk	1.83
Bath Soap	.62	Toothpaste	.76
Sunglasses	4.93		

First, add the prices to get the subtotal. Then find 4% of that and add it to get the total.

Subtotal = $26.14 ◄——————— Subtotal is before tax is added.
4% tax =   1.05 ◄——————— Tax is 4% of subtotal.
Total = $27.19 ◄——————— The sum gives you the total bill.

Ranzo, Anja, and Miro have each made a shopping list. Can you figure exactly how much each Arithmian will spend? (If necessary, round the amount of tax to the *next higher cent.*)

1.

RANZO

Shampoo	$ 2.44
Notebook	1.37
Deodorant	1.29
Eggs	.72
Milk	1.83
Salt	.35
Sugar	3.47
Cat Food	1.64

Subtotal _____
4% tax _____
Total _____

2.

MIRO

Laundry Soap	$ 5.16
Cereal	1.05
Rice	.39
Flour	3.09
Pencils	1.15
Radio	17.88
Crackers	.89
Toothpaste	.76

Subtotal _____
4% tax _____
Total _____

3.

ANJA

Potato Chips	$ 1.09
Ice Cream	1.10
Canned Soup	.24
Cookies	1.19
Bath Soap	.62
Scarf	3.86
Pencils	1.15
Toilet Paper	2.46

Subtotal _____
4% tax _____
Total _____

Use the price list shown below to fill in the prices for each item in the nine shopping lists. For each list, find the subtotal; then add 4% sales tax to get the total bill for each list. (When necessary, always round tax to the next higher cent.)

PRICE LIST

Ice Cream	$1.79	Eggs	$ .89	Pencils	$ .39
Flour	.71	Rice	1.12	Toilet Paper	.88
Sugar	1.04	Soup	.27	Garbage Bags	1.36
Lettuce	.49	Cookies	.98	Bath Soap	.42
Bread	.79	Potato Chips	.65	Bleach	1.14
Crackers	.84	Cereal	.78	Shampoo	1.19
Cake Mix	.62	Vitamins	4.98	Laundry Soap	2.37
Milk	1.85	Cat Food	4.64	Deodorant	1.53
Salt	.26	Dog Food	5.03	Scarf	2.83
Peanut Butter	1.29	Tooth Paste	1.29	Purse	7.82

Going Shopping

√ 1.

```
Cat Food
Flour
Sugar
Lettuce
Bread
Vitamins
Ice Cream
Toothpaste        _____
    Subtotal:
    4% Tax:  _____
    TOTAL:
```

√ 2.

```
Sugar
Crackers
Pencils
Toilet Paper
Cat Food
Scarf
Purse
Potato Chips      _____
    Subtotal:
    4% tax:  _____
    TOTAL:
```

3.

```
Cake Mix
Garbage Bags
Milk
Salt
Shampoo
Pencils
Bath Soap
Scarf             _____
    Subtotal:
    4% tax:  _____
    TOTAL:
```

4.

```
Pencils
Bleach
Dog Food
Rice
Peanut Butter
Eggs
Deodorant
Cookies           _____
    Subtotal:
    4% tax:  _____
    TOTAL:
```

5.

```
Rice
Flour
Bread
Cookies
Deodorant
Eggs
Laundry Soap
Toothpaste        _____
    Subtotal:
    4% tax:  _____
    TOTAL:
```

6.

```
Pencils
Bath Soap
Cat Food
Lettuce
Cake Mix
Salt
Soup
Scarf             _____
    Subtotal:
    4% tax:  _____
    TOTAL:
```

7.

```
Milk
Vitamins
Sugar
Crackers
Pencils
Flour
Lettuce
Garbage Bags      _____
    Subtotal:
    4% tax:  _____
    TOTAL:
```

8.

```
Dog Food
Toothpaste
Toilet Paper
Ice Cream
Sugar
Bread
Shampoo
Bleach            _____
    Subtotal:
    4% tax:  _____
    TOTAL:
```

9.

```
Peanut Butter
Eggs
Flour
Cookies
Bleach
Cereal
Garbage Bags
Milk              _____
    Subtotal:
    4% tax:  _____
    TOTAL:
```

Now that the Arithmians can estimate and figure exact total bills, including tax, they can see how easy it is to be short-changed when they go shopping.

SAMPLE:

Ranzo bought a tennis racquet for $16.67. If he paid with a $20.00 bill, how much change should he receive?

A.	B.	C.
$ .33 coins	$ .33 coins	$ .43 coins
4.00 bills	3.00 bills	3.00 bills

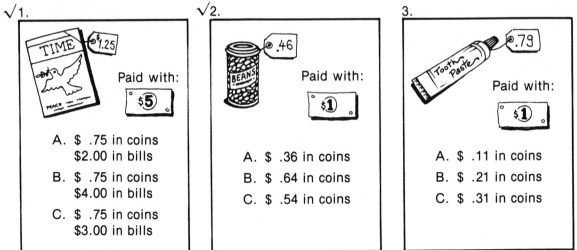

√1. TIME $1.25

Paid with: $5

A. $ .75 in coins
$2.00 in bills

B. $ .75 in coins
$4.00 in bills

C. $ .75 in coins
$3.00 in bills

√2. BEANS .46

Paid with: $1

A. $ .36 in coins

B. $ .64 in coins

C. $ .54 in coins

3. Tooth Paste .79

Paid with: $1

A. $ .11 in coins

B. $ .21 in coins

C. $ .31 in coins

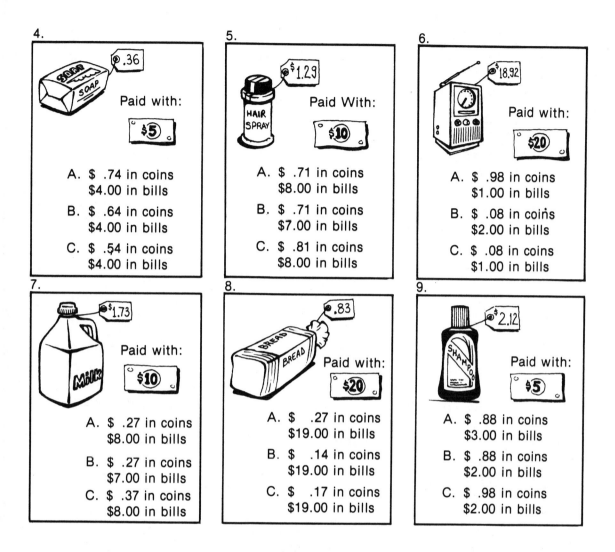

4.

SOAP @.36

Paid with: $5

A. $ .74 in coins
   $4.00 in bills

B. $ .64 in coins
   $4.00 in bills

C. $ .54 in coins
   $4.00 in bills

5.

HAIR SPRAY $1.23

Paid With: $10

A. $ .71 in coins
   $8.00 in bills

B. $ .71 in coins
   $7.00 in bills

C. $ .81 in coins
   $8.00 in bills

6.

$18.92

Paid with: $20

A. $ .98 in coins
   $1.00 in bills

B. $ .08 in coins
   $2.00 in bills

C. $ .08 in coins
   $1.00 in bills

7.

Milk $1.73

Paid with: $10

A. $ .27 in coins
   $8.00 in bills

B. $ .27 in coins
   $7.00 in bills

C. $ .37 in coins
   $8.00 in bills

8.

BREAD $.83

Paid with: $20

A. $ .27 in coins
   $19.00 in bills

B. $ .14 in coins
   $19.00 in bills

C. $ .17 in coins
   $19.00 in bills

9.

SHAMPOO $2.12

Paid with: $5

A. $ .88 in coins
   $3.00 in bills

B. $ .88 in coins
   $2.00 in bills

C. $ .98 in coins
   $2.00 in bills

Here are some more problems to figure in your head. On a separate sheet of paper, write down the letter which shows the correct amount of change you should receive.

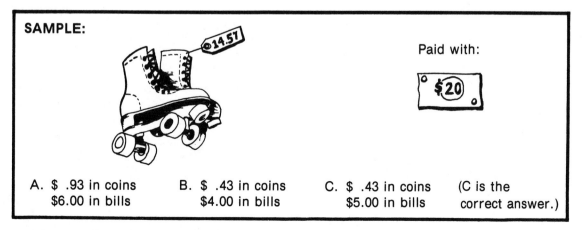

SAMPLE:

$14.57

Paid with: $20

A. $ .93 in coins   B. $ .43 in coins   C. $ .43 in coins   (C is the
   $6.00 in bills $4.00 in bills $5.00 in bills   correct answer.)

1. A hair brush, costing $1.61, paid with a $5 bill.

   A. $ .39 in coins
      $3.00 in bills

   B. $ .39 in coins
      $2.00 in bills

   C. $ .39 in coins
      $4.00 in bills

2. A can of soup, costing $.27, paid with a $1 bill.

   A. $ .83 in coins

   B. $ .36 in coins

   C. $ .73 in coins

3. A box of detergent, costing $3.35, paid with a $5 bill.

   A. $ .55 in coins
      $1.00 in bills

   B. $ .55 in coins
      $2.00 in bills

   C. $ .65 in coins
      $1.00 in bills

4. A flashlight, costing $2.49, paid with a $10 bill.

   A. $ .51 in coins
      $7.00 in bills

   B. $ .41 in coins
      $7.00 in bills

   C. $ .61 in coins
      $7.00 in bills

5. A roll of tape, costing $.84, paid with a $1 bill.

   A. $ .26 in coins

   B. $ .16 in coins

   C. $ .06 in coins

6. A record, costing $7.72, paid with a $10 bill.

   A. $ .28 in coins
      $1.00 in bills

   B. $ .28 in coins
      $3.00 in bills

   C. $ .28 in coins
      $2.00 in bills

7. Some doughnuts, costing $1.91, paid with a $20 bill.

   A. $ .09 in coins
      $18.00 in bills

   B. $ .19 in coins
      $18.00 in bills

   C. $ .28 in coins
      $18.00 in bills

8. A can of paint, costing $12.37, paid with a $20 bill.

   A. $ .73 in coins
      $7.00 in bills

   B. $ .63 in coins
      $7.00 in bills

   C. $ .63 in coins
      $8.00 in bills

9. A half gallon of ice cream, costing $1.64, paid with a $5 bill.

   A. $ .36 in coins
      $4.00 in bills

   B. $ .36 in coins
      $3.00 in bills

   C. $ .34 in coins
      $3.00 in bills

Chapter 1
Self-Test

For items 1-5, decide which of the four choices given is the correct price for the item selling at its discount. (See pages 7-14.)

1. A clock regularly priced $45.75, selling at a 20% discount.
   A. $26.75
   B. $35.00
   C. $36.60
   D. $41.35

2. A chair regularly priced $65.00, selling at a 10% discount.
   A. $62.98
   B. $59.00
   C. $61.38
   D. $58.50

3. A sweater regularly priced $18.69, selling at a 25% discount.
   A. $14.02
   B. $11.69
   C. $16.07
   D. $15.23

4. A hat regularly priced $6.36, selling at ⅓ off.
   A. $5.95
   B. $4.16
   C. $4.24
   D. $6.12

5. A fan regularly priced $29.38, selling at ½ off.
   A. $19.60
   B. $13.19
   C. $16.21
   D. $14.69

For items 6 and 7, figure the cost for each fraction of a unit. (See pages 14-17.)

6. ¼ lb. of candy selling at $2.68 per pound.

7. ¾ lb. of pork chops selling at $2.72 per pound.

For items 8 and 9, determine which of the four choices is the correct *total* for each shopping list. Use the price list below. (See pages 21-23.)

Price List			
Eggs	$ .79	Oatmeal	$ .69
Milk	1.10	Hamburger	1.89
Butter	1.59	Salt	.23
Bread	.75	Cheese	2.15
Toothpaste	.89	Applesauce	.47
Cookies	.99	Carrots	.44
Peanuts	4.25	Orange Juice	.99

8.

	A. $4.79
Bread	B. $3.99
Toothpaste	C. $5.98
Applesauce	D. $5.19
Cookies	
Hamburger	
Subtotal	
4% Tax	
Total	

9.

	A. $11.90
Oatmeal	B. $ 9.27
Salt	C. $ 9.44
Carrots	D. $ 7.64
Peanuts	
Butter	
Cheese	
Milk	
Cookies	
Subtotal	
4% Tax	
Total	

Round up the price on each list to the next higher half dollar or dollar. Choose the answer that is the best estimate of the total price. (See pages 17-20.)

10.

Item	Price	Rounded
Shirt	$16.30	
Shoes	$34.70	
Sweater	$24.93	
Jacket	$47.79	
Tie	$ 8.59	
Hat	$14.25	
	TOTAL	

A. $139.00
B. $148.00
C. $165.50
D. $148.27

Solve each of these problems. (See pages 24-28.)

11. Francisco gave a $10 bill for $3.76 worth of fruit. How much change will he receive?

12. Sandra gave a $5.00 bill to pay for $2.39 worth of hamburger. How much change will she receive?

13. Wally bought $34.16 worth of food. He paid with a $50.00 bill. How much change will he receive?

14. Gail bought sunglasses for $7.56. She paid with a $20.00 bill. How much change will she receive?

15. Jeremy bought a baseball glove for $12.98. He paid with a $20.00 bill. How much change will he receive?

CHAPTER

HAVING A JOB

USING BASIC MATH SKILLS TO SOLVE PROBLEMS RELATED TO HAVING A JOB.

KEY WORDS:

1. **Deductions:** on a pay stub, the amounts deducted from a worker's pay for such things as taxes and insurance.

2. **Pay Stub:** a piece of paper attached to a worker's pay check, which lists all the earnings and deductions.

3. **Gross Pay:** the total amount earned by a worker *before* deductions are made from the pay.

4. **Federal Withholding Tax:** a tax taken out of each pay check to go toward paying a worker's income tax. The employer figures how much to deduct from each worker's pay for taxes, and sends the money to Washington, D.C. Some of the withholding tax may be refunded to the worker.

5. **F.I.C.A.** Federal Insurance Contributions Act. This is the law which established the social security system in the U.S. Money withheld for social security is labeled "F.I.C.A.", and the worker receives this money back when he or she retires.

6. **Net Pay:** a worker's take-home pay. It is figured by subtracting all deductions from the worker's gross pay.

7. **Annual Pay:** the amount of money a worker earns in a year.

8. **Tip:** a small amount of money given directly to someone (a waiter or cab driver, for example) who performs a service. A tip is generally a percentage of the total bill for the service.

9. **Commission:** a percentage of the selling price of goods. Many salespersons earn commissions on the goods they sell.

10. **Earnings:** on a pay stub, a listing of rate of pay, the number of hours worked, and other information. The information on a pay stub explains the amount of gross pay earned by a worker for a certain period of time.

11. **Health Insurance:** a plan for which a worker pays to cover medical costs, in case he or she becomes ill. In some cases, the employer may pay for part or all of this insurance.

12. **Overtime:** work beyond the regularly scheduled hours of a job. A worker often receives a higher hourly rate for overtime work than for regularly scheduled work.

13. **Salary:** the weekly, monthly, or yearly (annual) amount which a job pays.

SKILL: Check the accuracy of take-home pay.

In order to support themselves, the Arithmians realize that they must have jobs. Miro gets a job at a local hamburger place, and soon has his first pay check.

Hamburger Haven

066424

2618 Leander Lane, Your City USA 65234

FIRST SAVINGS & TRUST BANK
YOUR CITY, USA

October 31, 19 80

$,***97 DOLLARS 60 CENTS $ 97.60

PAY
TO THE
ORDER OF

MIRO ARITHMIAN
6912 North Peanut Lane
Your City, USA

⑈066424⑈ ⑆0678⑈9037⑈ 312⑈167⑈9⑈

EARNINGS

WEEK ENDING	RATE	REGULAR HOURS	OVERTIME HOURS	REGULAR PAY	OVERTIME PAY	GROSS PAY
4 / 25	3.00	40	0	120.00	0	120.00

DEDUCTIONS

FEDERAL WITHHOLDING TAX	STATE WITHHOLDING TAX	F.I.C.A.	HEALTH INSURANCE	DUES	OTHER	NET PAY
10.10	3.54	6.76	2.00	0	0	97.60

PLEASE DETACH AND RETAIN FOR YOUR RECORDS

YOU SHOULD CASH THE PAYCHECK AND KEEP THE PAY STUB FOR YOUR RECORDS.

LOOK AT THE PAY STUB. SEE THE TOP ROW OF BOXES. THESE SHOW YOUR EARNINGS. IT SHOWS YOUR RATE ---$3.00 AN HOUR, AND YOUR HOURS. YOU WORKED 40 HOURS.

EARNINGS						
WEEK ENDING	RATE	REGULAR HOURS	OVERTIME HOURS	REGULAR PAY	OVERTIME PAY	GROSS PAY
4/25	3.00	40	0	120.00	0	120.00

DEDUCTIONS						
FEDERAL WITHHOLDING TAX	STATE WITHHOLDING TAX	F.I.C.A.	HEALTH INSURANCE	DUES	OTHER	NET PAY
10.10	3.54	6.76	2.00	0	0	97.60

PLEASE DETACH AND RETAIN FOR YOUR RECORDS

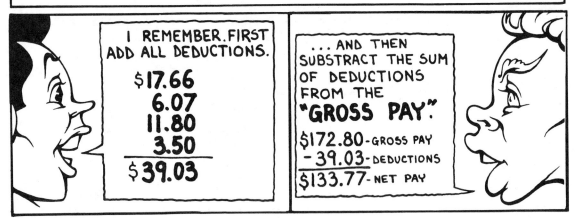

First, let's make sure we all understand how to check pay stubs.

Let's say I get a job and my pay check is for $132.77.

My pay stub would look something like this:

EARNINGS

WEEK ENDING	RATE	REGULAR HOURS	OVERTIME HOURS	REGULAR PAY	OVERTIME PAY	GROSS PAY
4/25	5.40	32	0	172.80	0	172.80

DEDUCTIONS

FEDERAL WITHHOLDING TAX	STATE WITHHOLDING TAX	F.I.C.A.	HEALTH INSURANCE	DUES	OTHER	NET PAY
17.66	6.07	11.80	3.50	0	0	132.77

PLEASE DETACH AND RETAIN FOR YOUR RECORDS

I remember. First add all deductions.

$17.66
6.07
11.80
3.50
$39.03

...and then substract the sum of deductions from the "GROSS PAY".

$172.80 - GROSS PAY
- 39.03 - DEDUCTIONS
$133.77 - NET PAY

Check the accuracy of net pay on these pay stubs by subtracting the total deductions from the gross pay. Which ones are correct? Which ones are not?

√
1.

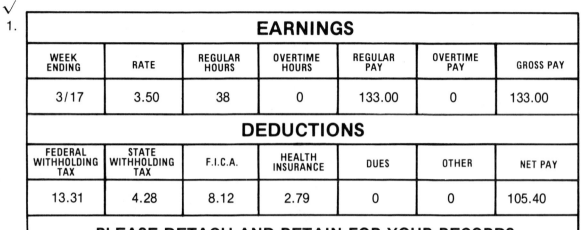

EARNINGS

WEEK ENDING	RATE	REGULAR HOURS	OVERTIME HOURS	REGULAR PAY	OVERTIME PAY	GROSS PAY
3/17	3.50	38	0	133.00	0	133.00

DEDUCTIONS

FEDERAL WITHHOLDING TAX	STATE WITHHOLDING TAX	F.I.C.A.	HEALTH INSURANCE	DUES	OTHER	NET PAY
13.31	4.28	8.12	2.79	0	0	105.40

PLEASE DETACH AND RETAIN FOR YOUR RECORDS

√
2.

EARNINGS

WEEK ENDING	RATE	REGULAR HOURS	OVERTIME HOURS	REGULAR PAY	OVERTIME PAY	GROSS PAY
5/29	4.80	26	0	124.80	0	124.80

DEDUCTIONS

FEDERAL WITHHOLDING TAX	STATE WITHHOLDING TAX	F.I.C.A.	HEALTH INSURANCE	DUES	OTHER	NET PAY
12.48	4.02	7.65	3.05	0	0	97.60

PLEASE DETACH AND RETAIN FOR YOUR RECORDS

3.

EARNINGS

WEEK ENDING	RATE	REGULAR HOURS	OVERTIME HOURS	REGULAR PAY	OVERTIME PAY	GROSS PAY
10/14	6.60	38.5	0	254.10	0	254.10

DEDUCTIONS

FEDERAL WITHHOLDING TAX	STATE WITHHOLDING TAX	F.I.C.A.	HEALTH INSURANCE	DUES	OTHER	NET PAY
25.41	8.17	15.57	5.84	0	0	198.11

PLEASE DETACH AND RETAIN FOR YOUR RECORDS

4.

EARNINGS

WEEK ENDING	RATE	REGULAR HOURS	OVERTIME HOURS	REGULAR PAY	OVERTIME PAY	GROSS PAY
1/15	5.72	35	0	200.20	0	200.20

DEDUCTIONS

FEDERAL WITHHOLDING TAX	STATE WITHHOLDING TAX	F.I.C.A.	HEALTH INSURANCE	DUES	OTHER	NET PAY
20.12	6.44	12.23	2.49	0	0	158.92

PLEASE DETACH AND RETAIN FOR YOUR RECORDS

5.

EARNINGS

WEEK ENDING	RATE	REGULAR HOURS	OVERTIME HOURS	REGULAR PAY	OVERTIME PAY	GROSS PAY
7/23	4.28	36.5	0	156.22	0	156.22

DEDUCTIONS

FEDERAL WITHHOLDING TAX	STATE WITHHOLDING TAX	F.I.C.A.	HEALTH INSURANCE	DUES	OTHER	NET PAY
15.63	5.03	9.54	3.55	0	0	102.47

PLEASE DETACH AND RETAIN FOR YOUR RECORDS

Having A Job

6.

EARNINGS

WEEK ENDING	RATE	REGULAR HOURS	OVERTIME HOURS	REGULAR PAY	OVERTIME PAY	GROSS PAY
3/19	7.84	39.25	0	307.72	0	307.72

DEDUCTIONS

FEDERAL WITHHOLDING TAX	STATE WITHHOLDING TAX	F.I.C.A.	HEALTH INSURANCE	DUES	OTHER	NET PAY
30.79	9.90	18.79	6.47	0	0	241.77

PLEASE DETACH AND RETAIN FOR YOUR RECORDS

Here are six more sample pay stubs. Check the ''Net Pay'' or take home pay on each stub. Which ones are correct? Which are not?

1.

EARNINGS

WEEK ENDING	RATE	REGULAR HOURS	OVERTIME HOURS	REGULAR PAY	OVERTIME PAY	GROSS PAY
10/14	4.80	35	0	168.00	0	168.00

DEDUCTIONS

FEDERAL WITHHOLDING TAX	STATE WITHHOLDING TAX	F.I.C.A.	HEALTH INSURANCE	DUES	OTHER	NET PAY
16.55	5.96	11.27	4.16	0	0	130.06

PLEASE DETACH AND RETAIN FOR YOUR RECORDS

2.

EARNINGS						
WEEK ENDING	RATE	REGULAR HOURS	OVERTIME HOURS	REGULAR PAY	OVERTIME PAY	GROSS PAY
11/27	5.24	28	0	146.72	0	146.72

DEDUCTIONS						
FEDERAL WITHHOLDING TAX	STATE WITHHOLDING TAX	F.I.C.A.	HEALTH INSURANCE	DUES	OTHER	NET PAY
13.27	3.99	9.47	3.54	0	0	106.45

PLEASE DETACH AND RETAIN FOR YOUR RECORDS

3.

EARNINGS						
WEEK ENDING	RATE	REGULAR HOURS	OVERTIME HOURS	REGULAR PAY	OVERTIME PAY	GROSS PAY
5/22	3.16	32	0	101.12	0	101.12

DEDUCTIONS						
FEDERAL WITHHOLDING TAX	STATE WITHHOLDING TAX	F.I.C.A.	HEALTH INSURANCE	DUES	OTHER	NET PAY
9.48	2.76	7.61	2.11	0	3.00	70.16

PLEASE DETACH AND RETAIN FOR YOUR RECORDS

4.

EARNINGS						
WEEK ENDING	RATE	REGULAR HOURS	OVERTIME HOURS	REGULAR PAY	OVERTIME PAY	GROSS PAY
6/26	6.72	37	0	248.64	0	248.64

DEDUCTIONS						
FEDERAL WITHHOLDING TAX	STATE WITHHOLDING TAX	F.I.C.A.	HEALTH INSURANCE	DUES	OTHER	NET PAY
23.92	8.16	15.49	0	15.00	0	185.89

PLEASE DETACH AND RETAIN FOR YOUR RECORDS

5.

EARNINGS

WEEK ENDING	RATE	REGULAR HOURS	OVERTIME HOURS	REGULAR PAY	OVERTIME PAY	GROSS PAY
7/11	4.28	27	0	115.56	0	115.56

DEDUCTIONS

FEDERAL WITHHOLDING TAX	STATE WITHHOLDING TAX	F.I.C.A.	HEALTH INSURANCE	DUES	OTHER	NET PAY
12.36	4.19	8.78	3.65	0	0	86.58

PLEASE DETACH AND RETAIN FOR YOUR RECORDS

6.

EARNINGS

WEEK ENDING	RATE	REGULAR HOURS	OVERTIME HOURS	REGULAR PAY	OVERTIME PAY	GROSS PAY
9/22	2.90	33.5	0	97.15	0	97.15

DEDUCTIONS

FEDERAL WITHHOLDING TAX	STATE WITHHOLDING TAX	F.I.C.A.	HEALTH INSURANCE	DUES	OTHER	NET PAY
10.70	3.43	5.04	0	0	0	77.98

PLEASE DETACH AND RETAIN FOR YOUR RECORDS

SKILL: Figure a job's weekly or monthly pay when you know the annual salary.

When Anja and Ranzo look for jobs, how can they figure a job's weekly or monthly pay when they know the annual salary?

THERE'S AN EASY WAY TO FIGURE THE WEEKLY OR MONTHLY PAY IF YOU KNOW THE YEARLY SALARY OF THE JOB.

Here are some of the jobs which the Arithmians saw advertised. See if you are ready to figure the weekly or monthly pay for each of these jobs. (Round your answer to the nearest dollar.)

SAMPLE:

Shoe Salesperson
$9,000 per year
Find monthly pay.

Divide yearly
pay by 12

```
        $750
   12 )$9000
        84
        60
        60
         0
         0
```

Monthly Pay: __$750__

SAMPLE:

Repairperson
$10,500 per year
Find weekly pay.

Divide yearly
pay by 52

```
         $201   (say $202)
   52 )$10,500
        104
         10
          0
        100
         52
         48
```

Weekly Pay: __$202__

√ 1. Clerk
$7,176 per yr.
Weekly Pay_____

√ 2. Cab Driver
$9,450 per yr.
Monthly Pay_____

3. Gas Station Attendant
$5,430 per yr.
Monthly Pay_____

4. Teacher
$10,580 per yr.
Monthly Pay_____

5. Sales Manager
$27,075 per yr.
Monthly Pay_____

6. Hairdresser
$8,654 per yr.
Weekly Pay_____

7. Editor
$12,000 per yr.
Weekly Pay_____

8. Artist
$11,500 per yr.
Monthly Pay_____

9. Typist
$7,684 per yr.
Weekly Pay_____

10. Mechanic
$13,648 per yr.
Monthly Pay_____

11. Desk Clerk
$10,400 per yr.
Monthly Pay_____

12. Fire Fighter
$15,842 per yr.
Weekly Pay_____

13. Engineer
$19,651 per yr.
Weekly Pay _____

14. Office Manager
$11,049 per yr.
Monthly Pay_____

15. Police Officer
$14,863 per yr.
Weekly Pay_____

Here are some other jobs the Arithmians saw advertised. The yearly salary is given for each of these jobs. Figure the weekly or monthly pay. (Round to the nearest dollar.)

1. Photographer
$10,850 per yr.
Monthly Pay_____

2. Buyer
$15,620 per yr.
Weekly Pay_____

3. Ticket Agent
$13,600 per yr.
Monthly Pay_____

4. Writer
$19,455 per yr.
Weekly Pay_____

5. Production Manager
$14,742 per yr.
Monthly Pay_____

6. Assembler
$9,850 per yr.
Monthly Pay_____

7. Secretary
$12,651 per yr.
Weekly Pay_____

8. Barber
$10,200 per yr.
Weekly Pay_____

9. Musician
$7,825 per yr.
Monthly Pay_____

10. Surveyor
$14,386 per yr.
Monthly Pay_____

11. Sales Person
$8,405 per yr.
Weekly Pay_____

12. Butcher
$15,636 per yr.
Monthly Pay_____

SAMPLE:

Dishwasher: $3.40 per hour
30 hour week

Multiply rate of pay
times number of hours

$3.40
x 30
$102.00

Weekly Pay: __$102__

The Arithmians also found advertisements for jobs with hourly pay rates. Figure the weekly pay for these jobs. Round to the nearest cent when necessary.

√ 1. Mechanic
$4.85 per hour
45 hour week

√ 2. Receptionist
$3.45 per hour
25 hour week

3. Billing Clerk
$3.89 per hour
30 hour week

4. Painter
$3.97 per hour
40 hour week

5. Gas Station Attendant
$3.40 per hour
23 hour week

6. Fire Fighter
$6.85 per hour
36 hour week

7. Secretary
$3.58 per hour
40 hour week

8. Nurse
$5.25 per hour
37.5 hour week

9. Telephone Repair Person
$7.20 per hour
35 hour week

10. Computer Operator
$5.28 per hour
38.5 hour week

11. Construction Worker
$8.56 per hour
45.5 hour week

12. Truck Driver
$7.65 per hour
40 hour week

Other hourly jobs the Arithmians saw advertised are shown below. Figure the weekly pay for these jobs. (Round to the nearest cent when necessary.)

1. Circus Clown
$3.75 per hour
20 hour week

2. Coach
$6.40 per hour
15 hour week

3. Laborer
$3.56 per hour
40 hour week

4. Mechanic
$9.65 per hour
46.5 hour week

5. Gardener
$3.75 per hour
30 hour week

6. Printer
$8.64 per hour
40 hour week

7. Cook
$4.05 per hour
36.5 hour week

8. Plumber
$10.95 per hour
28 hour week

9. Dog Catcher
$4.20 per hour
35 hour week

SKILL: Figure a job's total earnings when they include *tips* or *commissions.*

While looking for a job, Ranzo discovers that in some jobs he can earn more than just a salary. Waiters and waitresses, for example, earn *tips.* A *tip* is money paid by a customer for a personal service. Can you name some other types of jobs in which the worker earns tips?

When Anja goes job hunting, she learns about *commissions.* Most sales people earn a salary plus *commissions* on the goods they sell. A *commission* is a percentage of the selling price of the goods being sold.

The Arithmians find tips and commissions very interesting as they check into some jobs that Americans have. They try to find the total earnings of each person in the problem. See if you can.

√1. Jackie Smith trims fingernails at a beauty shop. She earns $98.50 a week plus an average tip of $1.25 from each customer. If she serves an average of 35 customers a week, what will her average total earnings be each week?

√2. Bob Gustafson makes $12,600 a year selling computers. He also earns a commission amounting to 5% of his total sales for the year. One year he sold $85,000 worth of computers. What where Bob's total earnings that year?

3. Juan Gomez sells real estate. He earns $853.00 per month plus 4% commission on the price of every house he sells. Last month Juan sold one house for $43,000. How much did he earn that month?

4. Mary Johnson is a hairdresser at the Hairy Head Salon. She earns $86.45 a week. She also gets an average tip of 75¢ from each customer. If she sets hair for 25 customers a week, what are her total earnings for that week?

5. Don Hall drives a taxi. He earns $625.60 a month. One month his weekly tips were $18.42, $27.63, $35.81, and $41.40. How much did he make in all that month?

6. Susie Lopez makes 7% commission on her total sales for the year. She also earns a yearly salary of $7,568.52. If she sells an average of $6,500 worth of goods a year, what are her total earnings for a year?

7. Harold Cartright sells shoes at a local shoe store. He earns $685 per month, plus a 15% commission on his sales. One month he sold $1500 worth of shoes. What were his total earnings for that month?

8. Mark Reilly is a waiter at the Chicken Corner. He earns $119.75 per week, plus an average of $25.40 a week in tips. What is his average weekly income?

Here are some additional jobs the Arithmians found out about. Figure the total earnings for each job.

1. Kyle Jones makes $13,460 a year selling jewelry. He also receives an 11% commission on all the jewelry he sells. If he sold $92,000 worth of jewelry last year, what was his yearly income?

2. Phil Rogers delivers papers for the Daily Bugle. He is paid $68.00 a month, and one month he received tips each week of $3.25, $2.60, $4.40, and $3.95. How much did Phil make that month?

3. Dick Williams sells cars at Honest Hal's used car lot. His yearly salary is $8,570, plus a 5% commission on his total sales. Last year he sold $32,560 worth of used cars. What was his total income for that year?

4. Harry Delman makes $1,150 a month selling musical instruments. Last month he sold $946.26 in instruments, from which he received an 8% commission. What were Harry's total earnings last month?

5. Anne Long is a waitress at The Happy Hamburger. She earns $95.52 a week. She also gets an average tip of $3.25 with every check she writes. Last week she wrote 35 checks. What were her total earnings for the week?

6. Tony Corwin sells yachts. He earns $635.76 a month plus a 9% commission on every yacht he sells. Last month he sold a $67,000 yacht. How much did Tony make last month?

7. Larry Jackson is a golf caddy. He earns $82.60 a week, plus tips. One week his tips were $5.00, $3.50, $6.00, $10.50, $2.00, $12.75, and $9.20. How much did Larry make that week?

8. Rick Young makes a 6.5% commission on his total clothing sales for the year. Besides his $8,246.95 salary, Rick sold $46,921 worth of clothes. What are his total earnings for the year?

9. Nick Needham makes $765.00 a month selling encyclopedias, plus a 45% commission on his monthly sales. One month he sold $1,100.46 worth of encyclopedias. How much did Nick make that month?

10. Nancy Moore makes $11,045 a year selling stereo equipment. In addition, she earns 6% on her total yearly sales. One year she sold $21,498 worth of equipment. What were her total earnings that year?

Having A Job

11. Kevin O'Hara is paid $342.70 a month to work as a bellboy. Last month he had weekly tips of $27.50, $31.45, $36.20, and $23.60. How much did he earn last month?

12. Angelo Bautista sells mobile homes. He is paid a monthly salary of $860.00, plus 7% of his monthly sales total. One month he sold 3 mobile homes, totaling $25,647.19. How much did Angelo earn that month?

SKILL: Figure the total pay of a job, including overtime.

SAMPLE:

Welder
Regular Hourly Pay = $8.00
Overtime Rate = 1.5
                (time and a half)

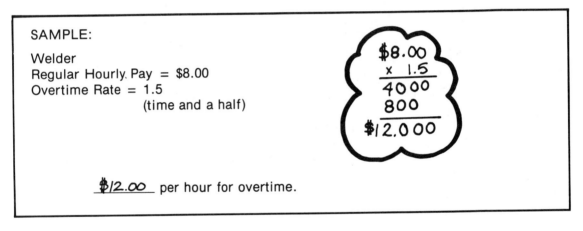

$12.00 per hour for overtime.

SAMPLE:

Welder
Hourly Rate for Overtime = $12.00
Overtime Hours This Week = 7

$12.00
× 7
$84.00

Total Overtime Pay: $84.00

Figure the total overtime earnings for these workers:

1.

Bulldozer Operator

Regular Hourly Pay	Overtime Rate
$6.20	1.5

Overtime Hours	Total Overtime Earnings
10	_____

2.

Window Washer

Regular Hourly Pay	Overtime Rate
$3.50	3.0

Overtime Hours	Total Overtime Earnings
12	_____

3.

Design Editor

Regular Hourly Pay	Overtime Rate
$2.58	2.0

Overtime Hours	Total Overtime Earnings
30	_____

NOW THAT YOU'VE FIGURED TOTAL OVERTIME PAY, IT'S EASY TO FIGURE THE JOB'S **TOTAL PAY,** INCLUDING OVERTIME.

ISN'T THAT THE SAME AS **GROSS PAY?**

RIGHT! YOU CAN SEE IT IN THIS PAY STUB.

EARNINGS

WEEK ENDING	REG. HRLY. PAY	REG. HOURS	REG. EARNINGS	OVERTIME HOURS	OVERTIME RATE	TOTAL OVERTIME EARNINGS	GROSS PAY
7/21	5.40	40	216.00	8	1.5	64.80	280.80

1. To find regular pay:
   multiply regular hourly pay
   times regular hours.
   $5.40 x 40 = $216.00

2. To figure overtime earnings,
   multiply regular hourly pay times
   overtime rate.
   $5.40 x 1.5 = $8.10
   . . . and multiply your answer
   by overtime hours.
   $8.10 x 8 = $64.80

3. To figure gross pay:
   add regular earnings and
   overtime earnings.
   $216.00 + 64.80 = $280.80

Complete each of the following pay stubs by figuring the *overtime,* and the *gross pay* for each. Round your answers to the nearest cent when necessary.

√

1.

EARNINGS

WEEK ENDING	REG. HRLY. PAY	REG. HOURS	REG. EARNINGS	OVERTIME HOURS	OVERTIME RATE	TOTAL OVERTIME EARNINGS	GROSS PAY
7/21	3.80	40		15	2.0		

Having A Job

2.

EARNINGS							
WEEK ENDING	REG. HRLY. PAY	REG. HOURS	REG. EARNINGS	OVERTIME HOURS	OVERTIME RATE	TOTAL OVERTIME EARNINGS	GROSS PAY
7/21	8.40	35		5	2.5		

3.

EARNINGS							
WEEK ENDING	REG. HRLY. PAY	REG. HOURS	REG. EARNINGS	OVERTIME HOURS	OVERTIME RATE	TOTAL OVERTIME EARNINGS	GROSS PAY
7/21	5.15	40		6	1.5		

4.

EARNINGS							
WEEK ENDING	REG. HRLY. PAY	REG. HOURS	REG. EARNINGS	OVERTIME HOURS	OVERTIME RATE	TOTAL OVERTIME EARNINGS	GROSS PAY
7/21	3.40	30		18	1.2		

5.

EARNINGS							
WEEK ENDING	REG. HRLY. PAY	REG. HOURS	REG. EARNINGS	OVERTIME HOURS	OVERTIME RATE	TOTAL OVERTIME EARNINGS	GROSS PAY
7/21	5.60	25		12	3		

6.

EARNINGS							
WEEK ENDING	REG. HRLY. PAY	REG. HOURS	REG. EARNINGS	OVERTIME HOURS	OVERTIME RATE	TOTAL OVERTIME EARNINGS	GROSS PAY
7/21	4.40	40		4	2		

7.

	EARNINGS						
WEEK ENDING	REG. HRLY. PAY	REG. HOURS	REG. EARNINGS	OVERTIME HOURS	OVERTIME RATE	TOTAL OVERTIME EARNINGS	GROSS PAY
7/21	7.90	35		17	1.6		

For additional practice in figuring the total pay of a job, complete each of these pay stubs. Figure the regular earnings, overtime, and gross pay for each stub. Round your answers to the nearest cent.

1.

	EARNINGS						
WEEK ENDING	REG. HRLY. PAY	REG. HOURS	REG. EARNINGS	OVERTIME HOURS	OVERTIME RATE	TOTAL OVERTIME EARNINGS	GROSS PAY
6/25	3.75	30		6	1.4		

2.

	EARNINGS						
WEEK ENDING	REG. HRLY. PAY	REG. HOURS	REG. EARNINGS	OVERTIME HOURS	OVERTIME RATE	TOTAL OVERTIME EARNINGS	GROSS PAY
7/1	4.14	26		10	2		

3.

	EARNINGS						
WEEK ENDING	REG. HRLY. PAY	REG. HOURS	REG. EARNINGS	OVERTIME HOURS	OVERTIME RATE	TOTAL OVERTIME EARNINGS	GROSS PAY
7/8	5.10	40		3	1.8		

4.

EARNINGS

WEEK ENDING	REG. HRLY. PAY	REG. HOURS	REG. EARNINGS	OVERTIME HOURS	OVERTIME RATE	TOTAL OVERTIME EARNINGS	GROSS PAY
7/15	3.50	37		1.5	1.5		

5.

EARNINGS

WEEK ENDING	REG. HRLY. PAY	REG. HOURS	REG. EARNINGS	OVERTIME HOURS	OVERTIME RATE	TOTAL OVERTIME EARNINGS	GROSS PAY
7/21	4.68	35		15	2.2		

6.

EARNINGS

WEEK ENDING	REG. HRLY. PAY	REG. HOURS	REG. EARNINGS	OVERTIME HOURS	OVERTIME RATE	TOTAL OVERTIME EARNINGS	GROSS PAY
9/3	5.65	27		5.5	2		

7.

EARNINGS

WEEK ENDING	REG. HRLY. PAY	REG. HOURS	REG. EARNINGS	OVERTIME HOURS	OVERTIME RATE	TOTAL OVERTIME EARNINGS	GROSS PAY
9/10	6.00	25		10	1.4		

8.

EARNINGS

WEEK ENDING	REG. HRLY. PAY	REG. HOURS	REG. EARNINGS	OVERTIME HOURS	OVERTIME RATE	TOTAL OVERTIME EARNINGS	GROSS PAY
9/17	4.20	32		8	3		

9.

EARNINGS							
WEEK ENDING	REG. HRLY. PAY	REG. HOURS	REG. EARNINGS	OVERTIME HOURS	OVERTIME RATE	TOTAL OVERTIME EARNINGS	GROSS PAY
9/24	3.60	38		2	1.2		

10.

EARNINGS							
WEEK ENDING	REG. HRLY. PAY	REG. HOURS	REG. EARNINGS	OVERTIME HOURS	OVERTIME RATE	TOTAL OVERTIME EARNINGS	GROSS PAY
9/31	3.75	20		9	1.8		

Chapter 2
Self-Test

For items 1-4, decide which answer is the correct one. (See pages 45-47.)

1. Pedro has a yearly salary of $11,500. How much does he make per month?
   A. $946.27   B. $958.33   C. $826.14   D. $1,458.16

2. A salesperson makes $23,504 per year. What does this salesperson earn weekly?
   A. $514.00   B. $469.10   C. $425.57   D. $452.00

3. Jason works 40 hours per week at $4.25 per hour. How much does he make per week?
   A. $170.00   B. $270.75   C. $196.50   D. $179.82

4. Belinda works a 46 hour week at $6.65 an hour. How much does she make per week?
   A. $305.90   B. $286.20   C. $307.90   D. $239.41

5. Lupe makes $9.50 per hour. What is her pay for a 25.5 hour week?
   A. $327.50   B. $217.25   C. $394.35   D. $242.25

For items 6 and 7, find the correct *NET PAY* for each pay stub. (See pages 33-45.)

6.

EARNINGS						
WEEK ENDING	RATE	REGULAR HOURS	OVERTIME HOURS	REGULAR PAY	OVERTIME PAY	GROSS PAY
8/23	4.00	35.5	0			142.00
DEDUCTIONS						
FEDERAL WITHHOLDING TAX	STATE WITHHOLDING TAX	F.I.C.A.	HEALTH INSURANCE	DUES	OTHER	NET PAY
26.23	7.00	8.70	1.50	0	0	
PLEASE DETACH AND RETAIN FOR YOUR RECORDS						

7.

EARNINGS						
WEEK ENDING	RATE	REGULAR HOURS	OVERTIME HOURS	REGULAR PAY	OVERTIME PAY	GROSS PAY
7/26	8.00	40	8	320.00	64.00	384.00

DEDUCTIONS						
FEDERAL WITHHOLDING TAX	STATE WITHHOLDING TAX	F.I.C.A.	HEALTH INSURANCE	DUES	OTHER	NET PAY
38.42	16.00	23.43	0	5.00	0	

PLEASE DETACH AND RETAIN FOR YOUR RECORDS

Solve each problem for items 8-10. (See pages 49-53.)

8. Sergio earns a salary of $180 a week, plus tips. One week he made $27.85 in tips. How much did Sergio earn that week?

9. Marjorie makes $254.30 per week, plus tips. She averages $15 a week in tips. What are her monthly earnings?

10. Valery is a salesperson. She earns 3% commission on the goods she sells, plus her weekly $200 salary. What is her total pay for a week in which she sold $5,200 worth of goods?

For items 11-12, find the *GROSS PAY* for each pay stub. (See pages 53-59.)

11.

EARNINGS							
WEEK ENDING	REG. HRLY. PAY	REG. HOURS	REG. EARNINGS	OVERTIME HOURS	OVERTIME RATE	TOTAL OVERTIME EARNINGS	GROSS PAY
5/19	6.50	40	260.00	2	2		

12.

EARNINGS							
WEEK ENDING	REG. HRLY. PAY	REG. HOURS	REG. EARNINGS	OVERTIME HOURS	OVERTIME RATE	TOTAL OVERTIME EARNINGS	GROSS PAY
10/5	5.00	35	175.00	10	1.5		

CHAPTER

FIXING THINGS UP

USING BASIC MATH SKILLS TO SOLVE PROBLEMS AROUND THE HOUSE.

KEY WORDS:

1. **Area:** the extent or size of any flat surface. It is found by multiplying the length by the width of the surface. The answer will be in square feet, square yards, square yards, square miles, etc.
2. **Gallon:** (of paint); the basic unit for buying paint.
3. **Height:** the number of feet from floor to ceiling.
4. **Length:** the number of feet in the long side of the room.
5. **Square Yard:** (of carpet); the basic unit for buying carpet.
6. **Unit:** the standard size in which a material is sold.
7. **Unit Price:** the cost of one unit of a material.
8. **Wallpaper Roll:** the basic unit for buying wallpaper.

1. Wallpaper comes in *rolls*.
2. Carpeting comes by the *square yard*.
3. Paint is cheapest by the *gallon*.

Step 1:
Measure length of each wall.

Wall 1 __11__ ft.
Wall 2 __16__ ft.
Wall 3 __11__ ft.
Wall 4 __16__ ft.

Step 2:
Add the lengths together.
11 ft.
16 ft.
11 ft.   Answer __54 ft.__
+ 16 ft.
_____
54 ft.

Step 3:
Multiply the answer from Step 2 by the height of the room.
Height: 8 ft.
Answer from Step 2: __54 ft.__

54 ft.
x 8 ft.
_____
432 sq. ft. is the *area.*

Fixing Things Up

SAMPLE:

A huge room is 80 ft. by 40 ft. This means that 2 walls are 80 ft. long and 2 walls are 40 ft. long. The height of the room is 10 ft. About how many gallons of paint are needed to cover the walls?

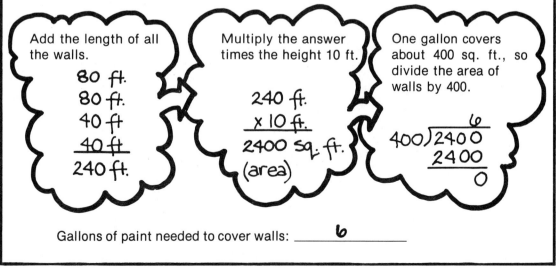

Add the length of all the walls.

80 ft.
80 ft.
40 ft.
40 ft.
240 ft.

Multiply the answer times the height 10 ft.

240 ft.
x 10 ft.
2400 sq. ft.
(area)

One gallon covers about 400 sq. ft., so divide the area of walls by 400.

400)2400 = 6
2400
0

Gallons of paint needed to cover walls: _____6_____

Figure the number of gallons needed to paint the following rooms with one coat of paint. Round off to the nearest gallon.

√ 1. A room is
15' x 22'. The
height is 10'.
_____gallons

√ 2. A room is
95' x 60'. The
height is 9'.
_____gallons

3. A room is
10' x 10'. The
height is 10'.
_____gallons

4. A room is
24½' x 13½'. The
height is 9'.
_____gallons

5. A room is
8' x 5'. The
height is 10'.
_____gallons

6. A room is
30' x 15'. The
height is 12'.
_____gallons

7. A room is
9' x 9'. The
height is 10'.
_____gallons

8. A room is
42' x 43'. The
height is 16'.
_____gallons

9. A room is
13' x 14½'. The
height is 8'.
_____gallons

10. A room is
25½' x 38½'. The
height is 10'.
_____gallons

11. A room is
50' x 35'. The
height is 12'.
_____gallons

12. A room is
60' x 80'. The
height is 8'.
_____gallons

13. A room is
20' x 35'. The
height is 8'.
_____gallons

14. A room is
8' x 11'. The
height is 8'.
_____gallons

15. A room is
12½' x 25½'. The
height is 10'.
_____gallons

Here are some more problems about how much paint is needed to cover different rooms with one coat of paint. Remember, one gallon covers about 400 sq. ft., so divide the area of the walls by 400. Round off to the nearest gallon.

1. A room is
68' x 68'. The
height is 12'.
_____gallons

2. A room is
29' x 30'. The
height is 10'.
_____gallons

3. A room is
40' x 45'. The
height is 8'.
_____gallons

4. A room is
10' x 18'. The
height is 10'.
_____gallons

5. A room is
5' x 10'. The
height is 9'.
_____gallons

6. A room is
20' x 30'. The
height is 8'.
_____gallons

7. A room is
40' x 50'. The
height is 16'.
_____gallons

8. A room is
15' x 15'. The
height is 10'.
_____gallons

9. A room is
15' x 30'. The
height is 12'.
_____gallons

Fixing Things Up

10. A room is
30' x 16'. The
height is 8'.
_____gallons

11. A room is
20' x 24'. The
height is 10'.
_____gallons

12. A room is
50' x 45'. The
height is 9'.
_____gallons

13. A room is
33' x 40'. The
height is 10'.
_____gallons

14. A room is
22½' x 20'. The
height is 12'.
_____gallons

15. A room is
75' x 25'. The
height is 10'.
_____gallons

16. A room is
30' x 25'. The
height is 8'.
_____gallons

17. A room is
58' x 41'. The
height is 15'.
_____gallons

18. A room is
60' x 80'. The
height is 9'.
_____gallons

SKILL: Figuring how many rolls of wallpaper are needed.

LET'S NOT FORGET THE WALLPAPER.

I'VE HEARD THAT WALLPAPER COMES IN ROLLS.

YES, IT DOES. EACH ROLL WILL COVER ABOUT 30 SQUARE FEET.

THERE ARE THOSE "SQUARE FEET" AGAIN.

SAMPLE:

A living room is 25 ft. by 20 ft., with a ceiling that is 9 ft. high. How many rolls of wallpaper are needed to cover all four walls?

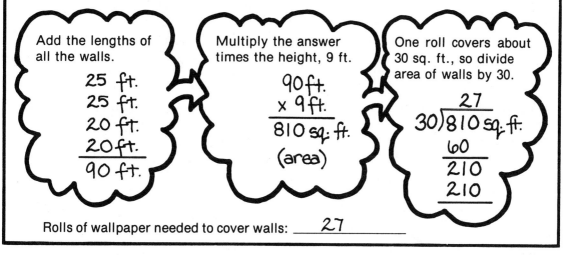

Add the lengths of all the walls.

$$\begin{array}{r} 25 \text{ ft.} \\ 25 \text{ ft.} \\ 20 \text{ ft.} \\ 20 \text{ ft.} \\ \hline 90 \text{ ft.} \end{array}$$

Multiply the answer times the height, 9 ft.

$$\begin{array}{r} 90 \text{ ft.} \\ \times\ 9 \text{ ft.} \\ \hline 810 \text{ sq. ft.} \end{array}$$

(area)

One roll covers about 30 sq. ft., so divide area of walls by 30.

$$\begin{array}{r} 27 \\ 30\overline{)810 \text{ sq. ft.}} \\ \underline{60} \\ 210 \\ \underline{210} \end{array}$$

Rolls of wallpaper needed to cover walls: ___27___

THAT'S FINE! NOW TRY THESE 6 PROBLEMS.

Round off to the nearest roll.

✓1. A room is 12' x 14' with a 9' ceiling. Rolls needed _____

✓2. A room is 13' x 11' with an 8' ceiling. Rolls needed _____

3. A room is 14' x 6' with a 7½' ceiling Rolls needed _____

4. A room is 23' x 10½' with a 9½' ceiling Rolls needed _____

5. A room is 14½' x 9½' with a 10½' ceiling. Rolls needed _____

6. A room is 18' x 7' with a 7' ceiling. Rolls needed _____

Figure out how many rolls of wallpaper are needed for these rooms. Remember, one roll of wallpaper covers 30 sq. ft. Round off to the nearest roll.

1. A room is 10' x 14'
   with an 8' ceiling.
   Rolls needed _____

2. A room is 12' x 16'
   with an 9' ceiling.
   Rolls needed _____

3. A room is 15' x 11'
   with an 11' ceiling
   Rolls needed _____

4. A room is 22½' x 20'
   with a 12' ceiling.
   Rolls needed _____

5. A room is 18' x 25½'
   with an 8' ceiling
   Rolls needed _____

6. A room is 18½' x 12½'
   with a 10' ceiling.
   Rolls needed _____

7. A room is 22' x 30'
   with an 11½' ceiling
   Rolls needed _____

8. A room is 15½' x 15'
   with a 13' ceiling.
   Rolls needed _____

9. A room is 18½' x 19½'
   with a 12' ceiling.
   Rolls needed _____

10. A room is 50' x 38'
    with a 15' ceiling.
    Rolls needed _____

11. A room is 26½' x 17½'
    with a 10' ceiling.
    Rolls needed _____

12. A room is 14' x 18'
    with a 9' ceiling.
    Rolls needed _____

SKILL: Figuring how many square yards of carpeting are needed to cover a floor.

The Arithmians have finished painting and wallpapering. Now, they are anxious to buy their new carpeting.

DOES CARPETING COME IN ROLLS LIKE WALLPAPER?

NO. I LEARNED ON T.V. THAT PEOPLE BUY CARPETING BY THE SQUARE YARD.

Fixing Things Up

SAMPLE:

How much carpet is needed in a room that is 18 ft. by 22 ft.?

Multiply length times width.

$$
\begin{array}{r}
22 \text{ ft.} \\
\times 18 \text{ ft.} \\
\hline
176 \\
22 \\
\hline
396 \text{ sq. ft.} \\
\text{(area)}
\end{array}
$$

Since there are 9 sq. ft. in 1 sq. yd., divide the number of square feet by 9 to get the square yards.

$$
\begin{array}{r}
44 \text{ sq. yds.} \\
9\overline{)396} \text{ sq. ft.} \\
\underline{36} \\
36 \\
\underline{36}
\end{array}
$$

Number of square yards of carpet needed = __44__

Figure out how much carpeting would be needed for these rooms. If the answers are not in whole numbers, round your answers to the next higher square yard.

√ 1. A bedroom, 17½' x 9'
_____ sq. yds.

√ 2. A hallway, 5' x 36'
_____ sq. yds.

3. A bedroom, 15' x 15'
_____ sq. yds.

4. A pantry, 6½' x 8'
_____ sq. yds.

5. A kitchen, 11½' x 13'
_____ sq. yds.

6. A banquet hall, 60' x 34½'
_____ sq. yds.

7. A clothing store, 35' x 56'
_____ sq. yds.

8. A porch, 12' x 17½'
_____ sq. yds.

For more practice, figure out how much carpeting would be needed for these rooms. If necessary, round your answers to the next higher square yard.

1. A bedroom, 15' x 12'
_____ sq. yds.

2. A closet, 5' x 7'
_____ sq. yds.

3. A kitchen, 20' x 12'
_____ sq. yds.

4. A laundry room, 12' x 12'
_____ sq. yds.

5. A bathroom, 8' x 15'.
_____ sq. yds.

6. A dining room, 16' x 15'
_____ sq. yds.

7. A recreation room, 20' x 20'
_____ sq. yds.

8. A nursery room, 13' x 12'
_____ sq. yds.

SKILL: Determining the cost of materials.

When the Arithmians bought their paint, wallpaper, and carpeting, they learned about figuring the cost of their materials. They found out how to determine the total cost of each material.

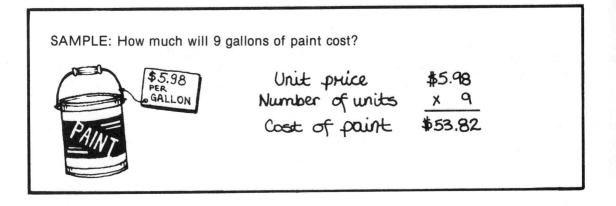

SAMPLE: How much will 9 gallons of paint cost?

Unit price $5.98
Number of units   x   9
Cost of paint $53.82

In the following problems, find the total cost of materials.

✓ 1. The paint you need is $11.98 a gallon. You need 3 gallons. You also need a paint brush for $4.97. How much in all?

✓ 2. The carpet you picked out is $13.23 a yard. You need 16 yards. You also need a carpet knife that costs $3.24. How much in all?

3. You need 9 rolls of wallpaper that cost $7.58 a roll. You also need a $2.78 scraper. How much in all?

4. You need 16 rolls of wallpaper and it is priced at $4.99 a roll. You also need $2.50 worth of wallpaper paste and a $4.87 brush.

5. A sale on carpeting has lowered the price to $4.98 per yard, and you want 65 yards. You also need $2.89 worth of carpet tacks.

6. Paint is $7.98 a gallon and wallpaper is $3.97 a roll. You need 9 gallons of paint, 11 rolls of wallpaper, a $6.49 paint brush, and a $9.97 wallpapering kit.

7. Paint is $8.79 a gallon, carpeting is $11.39 a yard, and wallpaper is $6.29 a roll. You'll need 3 gallons of paint, 14 rolls of paper, and 9 yards of carpet, plus a $7.69 paint brush and a $4.93 carpet knife.

8. You need 13 gallons of paint, 6 rolls of paper and 32 yards of carpeting. Paint is $9.69 a gallon, paper is $3.99 a roll, and carpeting is $7.59 a yard. You also need a $3.59 paint rolling kit, a $5.69 wallpapering kit, and a $3.89 carpet knife.

9. Carpeting is $6.98 a yard and wallpaper is $2.94 a roll. You need 80 yards of carpeting and 8 rolls of wallpaper, plus a wallpapering kit costing $9.79.

10. You need 18 rolls of paper and 4 gallons of paint. Paper is $5.98 a roll and paint is $11.93 a gallon. You also need a $6.97 paint brush.

11. For this job you'll need 42 yards of carpeting, 16 rolls of paper, 3 gallons of paint, a brush costing $8.97, and a wallpapering kit worth $11.93. Carpeting is $7.98 a yard, paint is $9.95 a gallon, and wallpaper is $3.98 a roll.

12. This job will require 12 rolls of paper costing $7.93 each, 4 gallons of paint costing $11.97 a gallon, and 21 yards of carpeting costing $5.97 a yard. In addition, you lost all your tools, so you'll need a $15.98 painting kit, an $11.93 wallpapering kit, and a $6.97 carpet knife.

For more practice, figure out the total cost of materials for each of the following projects.

1. To remodel this room, you will need 40 square yards of carpet, 15 rolls of wallpaper, and 1 gallon of paint. You also need a drop cloth costing $1.98, a brush costing $4.95, and wallpaper paste costing $7.47. Carpeting is $8.42 per square yard, wallpaper is $3.27 per roll, and paint is $8.50 per gallon.

2. This job requires 4 gallons of paint and 20 square yards of carpeting. Paint is $7.87 a gallon and carpeting is $10.41 a square yard. Also needed is a painting kit at $11.88 and paint thinner for $1.89.

3. Wallpaper is $3.27 a roll, carpet is $9.99 a square yard, and paint is $8.04 a gallon. You need 11 rolls of paper, 30 square yards of carpet, and 4 gallons of paint. You also need a paint brush for $4.28, a rolling pan for $3.87, and a ladder for $27.87.

4. You need 15 square yards of carpet at $8.52 a square yard, 12 rolls of wallpaper at $3.08 a roll, and 8 gallons of paint at $7.52 a gallon. You also need a roll of masking tape at $1.27 a roll, and a wallpapering kit for $10.88.

5. You need 6 gallons of paint and 22 rolls of wallpaper. Also you need a paint roller and pan costing $7.56 and a dropcloth priced at $3.89. The paint costs $6.47 a gallon and the wallpaper is $4.16 a roll.

6. To fix up the hallway you require 10 square yards of carpet and 3 gallons of paint. You also need a $13.26 light fixture. Carpet sells for $8.80 a square yard and paint is $5.84 a gallon.

7. A job takes 4 gallons of paint, 10 rolls of wallpaper, and 16 square yards of tile. Besides these items, it requires a $7.68 wallpapering kit and a $3.92 paint scraper. The paint is $7.44 a gallon, the tile is $2.98 a square yard, and the wallpaper is $4.98 a roll.

8. You must have 80 square yards of carpet and 8 gallons of paint to finish remodeling the dining room. You also need a carpet pad costing $127.65. The carpet is priced at $4.81 a square yard, and the paint is $6.68 a gallon.

9. A job requires 5 gallons of paint and 22 rolls of wallpaper. In addition, you need a $3.42 roller pad. The paint costs $4.18 a gallon, and the wallpaper is $5.11 a roll.

10. Carpet costs $6.87 a square yard, and paint goes for $5.78 a gallon. You'll need 19 square yards of carpet and 2 gallons of paint. Also, you'll need a pair of carpet shears costing $8.96 and a box of carpet tacks selling for $.89.

11. To decorate the bedroom you want 3 gallons of paint and 9 rolls of wallpaper. You also want a shelf costing $19.61 and a lamp costing $13.22. The paint is $5.81 a gallon, and the paper is $3.27 a roll.

12. A job takes 14 square yards of carpet and 4 gallons of paint. The carpet is $7.36 a square yard, and the paint is $4.90 a gallon. Also, you must have 16 rolls of wallpaper costing $4.21 a roll. What is worse, your ladder broke, and you must replace it with a new one priced at $37.82.

Now see if you can *combine* the skills from this chapter to solve these four problems. Round paint and wallpaper to the nearest gallon or roll. Round carpet to the next higher square yard.

√ 1. The den is 13 ft. x 11½ ft. with a 9 ft. ceiling. Wallpaper is $5.97 a roll. How much will it cost to paper the room?

2. The back room is 5 ft. x 21 ft., with a 9 ft. ceiling. How much will it cost to paint it with one coat? Paint is $9.97 a gallon, and you need a stepladder, which costs $14.59.

3. The floor in the living room is 24½ ft. x 14 ft. How much will it cost to carpet the floor, if carpeting is $13.97 a yard? You also need to rent a carpet stretcher, which costs $4.50.

4. The master bedroom is 25 ft. x 14½ ft. with a 9 ft. ceiling. Paint is $9.74 a gallon, and wallpaper is $6.53 a roll. You also need an $11.95 paint roller set and a $7.98 wallpapering kit. How much will it cost to paint the ceiling with one coat and wallpaper the walls?

Chapter 3
Self-Test

For items 1-5, write the correct answers on a separate sheet of paper. (See pages 67-76.)

1. A gallon of paint usually covers about _____ square feet.

2. A single roll of wallpaper usually covers about _____ square feet.

3. One square yard of carpet is equal to _____ square feet.

4. To find the area of a flat surface, multiply _____ x _____.

5. The standard size in which a material is sold is called a _____ .

For items 6-9, figure how many rolls of wallpaper would be needed to cover the walls. Round off the the nearest roll. (See pages 71-74.)

6. A room is 9 ft. x 12 ft. The height is 9 ft.

7. A room is 25 ft. x 13 ft. The height is 8 ft.

8. A room is 15 ft. x 16 ft. The height is 10 ft.

9. A room is 20 ft. x 14 ft. The height is 7½ ft.

For items 10-13, figure how many gallons of paint would be needed to cover the wall with one coat of paint. Round off to the nearest gallon. (See pages 67-71.)

10. A room is 11' x 12'. The height is 8'

11. A room is 26' x 12'. The height is 9'

12. A room is 11½' x 13'. The height is 7'

13. A room is 15' x 18'. The height is 10'

For items 14-17, figure how many square yards of carpet would be needed to cover the floor. Round to the next higher square yard. (See pages 74-76.)

14. A room is 15 ft. x 10 ft.

15. A room is 12 ft. x 14 ft.

16. A room is 25 ft. x 25 ft.

17. A room is 12½ ft. x 18 ft.

For items 18-20, figure out the total cost of materials. (See pages 76-80.)

18. Gail needs 3 gallons of paint. Each gallon costs $5.40. She also needs two paint brushes, which sell for $3.15 each, and a quart of paint thinner for 89¢. How much will this cost in all?

19. Allen needs 15 rolls of wallpaper. Each roll costs $7.98. He also needs 2 gallons of paint. Each gallon costs $5.49. How much will this cost in all?

20. The Marshall family needs 25 square yards of carpeting, which cost $9.00 per square yard. They also need a $3.00 carpet knife and $4.50 worth of carpet tacks. How much will all the materials cost them?

BUY NOW– PAY LATER

USING BASIC MATH SKILLS TO SOLVE PROBLEMS RELATED TO BUYING ON CREDIT.

KEY WORDS:

1. **Agreement:** a contract you sign showing that you agree to pay for goods you buy on credit plus the interest charged.
2. **Balance:** the amount of money you owe as shown on a bill or statement.
3. **Bill:** a piece of paper listing goods or services you have purchased and how much you owe.
4. **Credit:** a plan to delay full payment of a bill. When you buy on credit, you are allowed to pay a little at a time, rather than all at once. Buying on credit is more costly than paying with cash.
5. **Credit Card:** a plastic card that identifies you as a customer who can buy on credit.
6. **Credit Statement:** the bill you receive when you buy things with your credit card. It states how much you owe and the minimum amount due.
7. **Down Payment:** a cash payment you make when first making a purchase. It is

applied toward paying off what you owe.

8. **Finance Charge:** a charge you pay to buy on credit if you have not paid your bill in full. The finance charge is a percentage of the unpaid balance.

9. **Long Term Loan:** an amount of money you borrow and pay back over a long period of time, usually a year or more.

10. **Minimum Monthly Payment:** appears on a monthly credit card statement. It is the least amount of money you have to pay for purchases you have made on credit.

11. **Principal:** the amount of money you borrow from a bank or loan company.

12. **Rate of Interest:** a percentage you pay on money you borrow.

13. **Terms of Credit:** the specific details of how much you pay and for how long you pay when you buy on credit.

Buying on credit is something new to the Arithmians; in Arithmia they were used to paying immediately with *Cosmic Cash.* One day, they were almost trapped into paying a lot of extra money just to buy on credit. Luckily, Anja realized this in time, so the next day she went to a friend, who explained everything about credit to her. Now when she goes shopping, Anja is prepared to deal with the temptation of buying on credit.

SKILL: Figuring the extra cost when you buy on credit.

Miro and Ranzo were very glad Anja did not want to sign the salesman's credit agreement. If the Arithmians *had* signed it, they would be giving notice that they understood the terms of the ''agreement'', and that they were willing to pay what the terms of the credit demanded. Then, they would be required to make all 12 payments of $200.00 each.

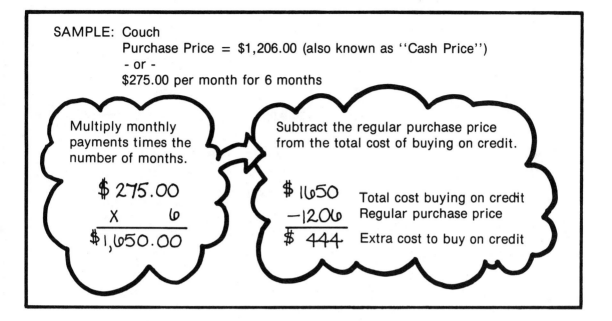

SAMPLE: Couch
   Purchase Price = $1,206.00 (also known as ''Cash Price'')
   - or -
   $275.00 per month for 6 months

Multiply monthly payments times the number of months.

$ 275.00
X   6
$1,650.00

Subtract the regular purchase price from the total cost of buying on credit.

$ 1650   Total cost buying on credit
−1206   Regular purchase price
$ 444   Extra cost to buy on credit

Figure the extra cost if you were to buy each of the following items on credit.

√ 1. Stereo
   Cash price = $450.00
      -or-
   $33.50 per month for 15 months

√ 2. Coat
   Cash price = $95.99
      -or-
   $35.00 per month for 3 months

3. Table and chairs
   Cash price = $1,020.00
      -or-
   $210.00 per month for 6 months

4. Television
   Cash price = $298.99
      -or-
   $26.50 per month for 12 months

5. Camera
   Cash price = $153.59
      -or-
   $21.50 per month for 9 months

6. Bicycle
   Cash price = $115.55
      -or-
   $40.00 per month for 3 months

7. Piano
   Cash price = $798.98
      -or-
   $72.13 per month for 12 months

8. Stove
   Cash price = $506.00
      -or-
   $25.00 per month for 24 months

9. Pool table
   Cash price = $1,415.99
      -or-
   $50.00 per month for 30 months

10. Truck
   Cash price = $9,104.39
      -or-
   $412.00 per month for 24 months

Math for Everyday Living

11. Radio
Cash price = $68.00
-or-
$5.20 per week for 15 weeks

12. Typewriter
Cash price = $278.50
-or-
$16.30 per week for 20 weeks

For more practice, figure the extra cost you would have to pay if you buy each of the following items on credit.

1. Toaster
Cash price = $47.23
or
$10.00 per week for 6 weeks

2. Vacuum cleaner
Cash price = $121.00
-or-
$25.50 per month for 6 months

3. Sewing Machine
Cash price = $251.60
-or-
$6.50 per week for 52 weeks

4. Car Stereo System
Cash price = $139.99
-or-
$12.50 per month for 12 months

5. Sofa
Cash price = $799.00
-or-
$50.00 per month for 18 months

6. Washing Machine
Cash price = $304.95
-or-
$60.00 per month for 6 months

7. Refrigerator
Cash price = $499.95
-or-
$49.00 per month for 12 months

8. Wrist Watch
Cash price = $218.25
-or-
$21.50 per month for 12 months

9. Home Stereo System
Cash price = $918.37
-or-
$56.00 per month for 18 months

10. Electric Lawn Mower
Cash price = $212.00
-or-
$40.00 per month for 6 months

11. Snowmobile
Cash price = $1,698.67
-or-
$99.00 per month for 18 months

12. Home Movie Projector
Cash price = $318.00
-or-
$14.00 per week for 26 weeks

SKILL: Figuring the amount of a *Down Payment* (given as a percentage or fraction).

SAMPLE: When the down payment is a fraction, figure it like this:

Work Boots: $65.80

¼ down

$\frac{1}{4}$ of $65.80 = $\frac{1}{4}$ × $65.80

$\frac{1}{4}$ × $\frac{\$65.80}{1}$ = $\frac{\$65.80}{4}$

$$\begin{array}{r} \$16.45 \\ 4\overline{)\$65.80} \\ \underline{4} \\ 25 \\ \underline{24} \\ 18 \\ \underline{16} \\ 20 \\ \underline{20} \end{array}$$

Down payment = $16.45

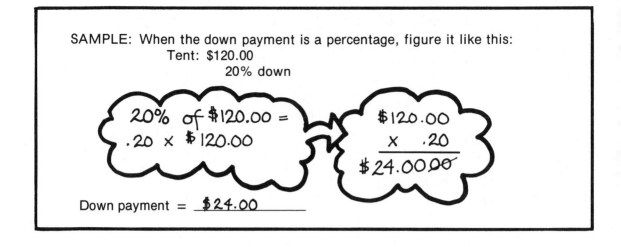

SAMPLE: When the down payment is a percentage, figure it like this:
Tent: $120.00
20% down

20% of $120.00 =
.20 × $120.00

$120.00
×   .20
$24.0000

Down payment = $24.00

Figure the down payment required for each of the following items. (Round to the nearest cent when necessary.)

√. House
$67,291.00
10% down payment

√ 2. Bicycle
$72.99
⅓ down payment

3. Washing Machine
$258.79
30% down payment

4. Suit
$195.89
20% down payment

5. Used Car
$3,243.00
15% down payment

6. Bedroom Furniture
$1,137.50
1/4 down payment

7. Stove
$636.48
1/5 down payment

8. Motorcycle
$1,652.91
10% down payment

9. Refrigerator
$468.44
10% down payment

For additional practice, figure out the down payment required for each of these items. Round to the nearest cent where necessary.

1. Dress
$87.55
20% down payment

2. Stereo Speakers
$397.49
¼ down payment

3. Ride-On Lawn Mower
$862.27
30% down payment

4. Clothes Dryer
$324.88
5% down payment

5. Carpets
$1,367.44
15% down payment

6. Ten Speed Bicycle
$272.10
1/3 down payment

7. Set of Radial Tires
$268.37
10% down payment

8. Land
$15,672.00
30% down payment

9. Motor Boat
$1,489.64
15% down payment

10. Trampoline
$238.74
20% down payment

11. Antique Clock
$1,112.43
¼ down payment

12. Executive Jet
$62,794.05
1/3 down payment

13. Special Van
$28,409.26
10% down payment

14. Fireplace
$738.60
¼ down payment

15. Color Television
$598.06
1/5 down payment

SKILL: Figuring the number of days to pay a *bill* after you receive it.

Ranzo, Anja, and Miro have learned they do not always have to pay for something right when they buy it. Instead, they realized they can be mailed "bills." These bills state how much they owe and when their payments are due.

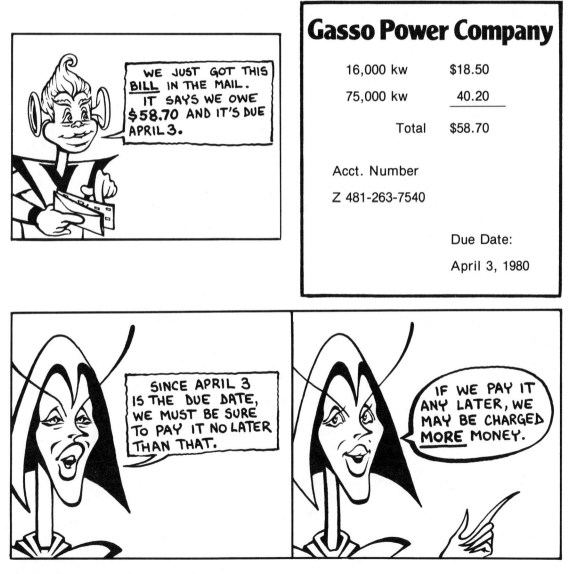

SAMPLE:

Bill received   March 21

Bill is due   April 3

First subtract to find how many days are left in March.

31 days in March
−21 date bill arrived
10 days left in March

Next, add this to how many days you have in April.

10 days left in March
+3 days in April
13 days to pay

HOW MANY MORE DAYS DO WE HAVE LEFT BEFORE WE HAVE TO PAY?

THAT'S NOT TOO HARD TO FIGURE OUT. LOOK:

THAT SOUNDS PRETTY EASY. LET'S SAY WE RECEIVE A BILL LIKE THIS ON SEPTEMBER 29.

Pat's fashion center

BILL

1 wool hat $25.00

Tax   .90

Total $25.90

Date Due:

October 16, 1980

SAMPLE:

Bill received   September 29

Bill is due   October 16

First, subtract to find how many days are left in September.

30 days in September
−29 date bill arrived
1 day left in September

Next, add this to how many days you have in October.

1 day left in September
+16 days in October
17 days to pay

Look at the following bills. Pretend that you received each bill on the date shown above that bill. Find the date each bill is due, and figure how many days are left before it is due.

✓ 1.   **Received Dec. 15, 1980**

DING·A·LING PHONE COMPANY ☎

This Bill is due: January 15, 1981

CALLED CHICAGO . . . . $ 150.25

CALLED HONG KONG 1,229.18

Tax   180.00

Total $1,559.33

✓ 2.   **Received July 3, 1980**

ACME RUG CO.

ACCT. NO.: 112	PAY BY JULY 31, 1980
1 shag rug, 9' x 12'	$500.98
2 small squares	4.50
Subtotal	505.48
Tax	14.00
TOTAL	$519.48

3. **Received October 28, 1980**

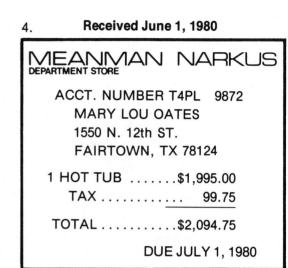

MAGIC CARPET FLYING SERVICE

JOE POLO
2828 Nuthatch Lane
Bodly, PA 00982

Acct. #6846-0-00982

1-WAY TICKET	
TO TIMBUKTU	$9,250.18
TAX	$ 800.00
YOU PAY	$10,050.18

DUE NOV. 15, 1980

4. **Received June 1, 1980**

MEANMAN NARKUS
DEPARTMENT STORE

ACCT. NUMBER T4PL 9872
MARY LOU OATES
1550 N. 12th ST.
FAIRTOWN, TX 78124

1 HOT TUB	$1,995.00
TAX	99.75
TOTAL	$2,094.75

DUE JULY 1, 1980

5. **Received May 4, 1980**

BOB'S Carpenter Shop

1 set cabinets $147.28

to: Joe Zeebo
296 Main
Plato, MO 41215

Due
May 15, 1980

6. **Received September 29, 1980**

R.U.WITTE, D.V.M.
427 A Ave.
Garble, VT 21508

SHOTS FOR 2 CATS	$15.64
WORM PILLS	2.00
	17.64
PLEASE PAY Tax:	1.02
BY OCT. 15, 1980	$18.66

Here are some more problems, for practice. Assume that you received the bill on the date noted. Take the date each bill is due and figure out how many days you have left to pay it.

1. Your bill from Greeble's Department Store comes on September 1, 1980. The bill is for $567.80, and is due on October 1, 1980. How many days do you have to pay the bill?

2. On January 5, 1981, you receive a bill from Toys, Inc., for $56.08, for the sled, doll, and dart board you bought for your nieces and nephews for Christmas. The bill must be paid by February 1, 1981. How many days until it is due?

Buy Now—Pay Later

3. On June 2, 1980, you receive a bill for $83.20 from the Arabique Oil Company, for the 160 gallons of fuel oil you bought during their "once in a lifetime" sale. The bill is due July 15, 1980. How many days before you must pay?

4. D.W. Abernathy, your favorite chiropractor, sent you his bill for $167.40 for treatments in May. You received the bill on June 6, 1980, and it is due July 1, 1980. How many days before it is due?

5. In July you hired Bill's Yard Service to do all the mowing, raking, pruning, and trimming which you did not have time to do. On August 1, 1980, you receive Bill's invoice for $88.80. It is due on August 15, 1980. How many days before you must pay Bill?

6. On November 16, 1980, you received a bill from Jim-Bob's Grocery, for $68.40. The bill is due December 15, 1980. How many days before the payment must be made?

SKILL: Figuring the *finance charge* on the balance of a bill.

Whenever Ranzo goes shopping, he notices the Americans paying for their purchases with little plastic cards. Ranzo learns these special cards are called "credit cards." He wonders how he can get one so he can buy anything he wants without spending any money. Ranzo decides he should ask Anja where he can get one of these *credit cards* that can buy so much without money.

Anja, however, disappoints him by explaining credit cards to him. She tells him that even though money is not needed at the time of the purchase, money *is* needed later because the buyer will get a *credit statement* in the mail.

WHAT'S A "CREDIT STATEMENT"?

IT SHOWS THE AMOUNTS OF MONEY YOU'VE CHARGED ON YOUR **CREDIT CARD**. IT WILL LOOK SOMETHING LIKE THIS:

MUSTERCHARGE, INC.

CREDIT STATEMENT

Wilz Weiner Walkaway	$ 17.83
Hickory Oaks Equipment Company	$ 18.54
Rutledge Plumbing Service	$122.26

Account Number	Minimum Amount Due	Due Date	Balance Due
A 75-QVR	$10.00	April 15, 1980	$158.63

Anja continues explaining the *credit statement* to Ranzo, and Miro becomes interested, too. She says the *balance due* is the total amount of money owed. If this full amount is paid by the *due date,* nothing extra is charged for buying on credit.

Buy Now—Pay Later

Finance Rate	Minimum Amount Due	Balance
1.5%	$12.34	$158.60

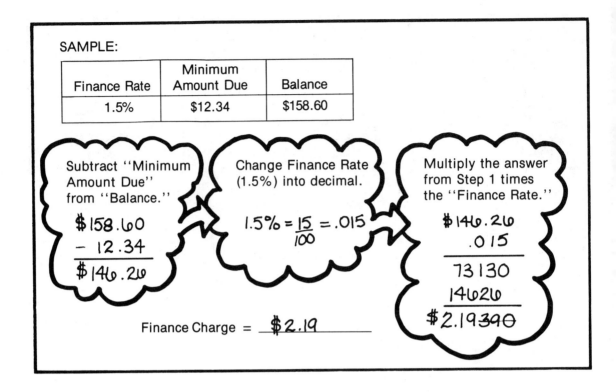

Subtract "Minimum Amount Due" from "Balance."

$$\begin{array}{r} \$158.60 \\ -\ 12.34 \\ \hline \$146.26 \end{array}$$

Change Finance Rate (1.5%) into decimal.

$$1.5\% = \frac{15}{100} = .015$$

Multiply the answer from Step 1 times the "Finance Rate."

$$\begin{array}{r} \$146.26 \\ .015 \\ \hline 73130 \\ 14626 \\ \hline \$2.19390 \end{array}$$

Finance Charge = $2.19

SAMPLE:

Finance Rate	Minimum Amount Due	Balance
1.5%	$10.00	$400.00

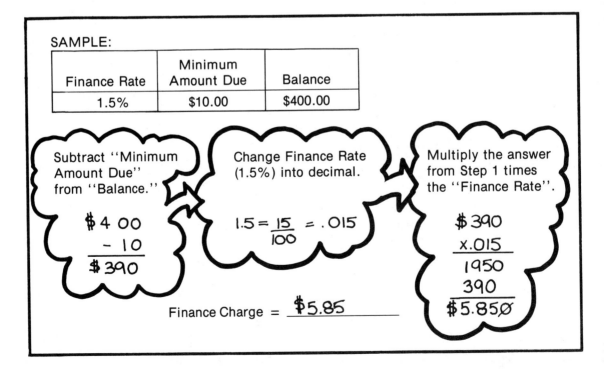

Subtract "Minimum Amount Due" from "Balance."

$$\begin{array}{r} \$4\ 00 \\ -\ 10 \\ \hline \$390 \end{array}$$

Change Finance Rate (1.5%) into decimal.

$$1.5 = \frac{15}{100} = .015$$

Multiply the answer from Step 1 times the "Finance Rate".

$$\begin{array}{r} \$390 \\ \times .015 \\ \hline 1950 \\ 390 \\ \hline \$5.850 \end{array}$$

Finance Charge = $5.85

For each of the following credit statements, figure the finance charge that will appear on the next monthly statement. Assume only the *minimum amount due* is paid. (Round your answers to the nearest cent.)

√1.

Finance Rate	Minimum Amount Due	Balance
1.0%	$11.52	$395.60

Finance charge _____

√2.

Finance Rate	Minimum Amount Due	Balance
1.4%	$12.18	$527.82

Finance charge _____

3.

Finance Rate	Minimum Amount Due	Balance
1.5%	$12.93	$218.91

Finance charge _____

4.

Finance Rate	Minimum Amount Due	Balance
1.1%	$13.81	$418.73

Finance charge _____

5.

Finance Rate	Minimum Amount Due	Balance
1.0%	$10.53	$162.50

Finance charge _____

6.

Finance Rate	Minimum Amount Due	Balance
.5%	$100.00	$3,800.00

Finance charge _____

Here are some additional credit card statements. For each, figure the *finance charge* that will appear on the next monthly statement. Assume that only the *minimum amount due* is paid. Round your answers to the nearest cent.

1. Finance Rate | Minimum Amount Due | Balance
   1.5% | $24.00 | $376.00

   Finance charge _____

2. Finance Rate | Minimum Amount Due | Balance
   1.8% | $12.50 | $98.00

   Finance charge _____

3. Finance Rate | Minimum Amount Due | Balance
   .075% | $17.00 | $48.00

   Finance charge _____

4. Finance Rate | Minimum Amount Due | Balance
   1.8% | $70.00 | $2,173.00

   Finance charge _____

5. Finance Rate | Minimum Amount Due | Balance
   1.0% | $12.98 | $47.00

   Finance charge _____

6. Finance Rate | Minimum Amount Due | Balance
   1.0% | $56.00 | $640.00

   Finance charge _____

SKILL: Determining monthly payents when *long term credit* is arranged.

The Arithmians are becoming very interested in credit. Ranzo has just learned that money can be borrowed from banks and is very excited about it. Anja, however, has already been to a bank and learned all about *long term loans.*

SO TELL US WHAT YOU LEARNED ABOUT CREDIT FROM THE BANK, ANJA.

WHEN MONEY IS BORROWED FROM A BANK, THE AMERICANS PAY "INTEREST".

1. How *much* you borrow (this is called the "principal").

2. Rate of interest (this is always a percentage).

3. How much time you have to pay the money back.

SAMPLE: What is the *"interest"* if $1000 is borrowed at 10% interest for 2 years?

Multiply principal x rate.

$1000 Principal
x .10 Rate—decimal form
$100

Multiply answer from Step 1 x time.

$100 interest for 1 year
x 2 number of years
$200

Total interest for 2 years $200

NOW, TRY TO PUT IT ALL TOGETHER.

SAMPLE: What is the monthly payment for this loan?
$4,200 at 8% interest for 4 years.

Figure the interest for one year.

$ 4200 principal
x   .08 rate - decimal form
$336.00

Multiply yearly interest times the number of years.

$ 336 yearly interest
x   4 number of years
$1344

Add total interest to the amount you are borrowing.

$ 4200
  1344
$ 5544

Divide total by the number of months you will have the loan.

(4 years = 48 months)

```
        $   115.50
    48) $5544.00
        48
        74
        48
        264
        240
        240
        240
        00
```

Monthly payments = $115.50

Figure the monthly payments for each of the following long term loans. Round to the nearest cent if necessary.

√ 1. $1,500 at 12% for 3 years.

√ 2. $750 at 11% for 2 years.

3. $20,000 at 7% for 15 years.

4. $1,800 at 9% for 5 years.

5. $150 at 12% for 1 year.

6. $120,000 at 5% for 10 years.

7. $16,500 at 10% for 3 years.

8. $7,500 at 11% for 12 years.

For more practice, figure the monthly payments for each of the following long term loans. Round to the nearest cent if necessary.

1. $26,000 at 9% for 15 years.

2. $1,750 at 13% for 3 years.

3. $12,000 at 7% for 10 years.

4. $500 at 8% for 1 year.

5. $250 at 4% for 1 year.

6. $4,800 at 12% for 2 years.

7. $150,000 at 8% for 20 years.

8. $36,500 at 11% for 25 years.

Buy Now—Pay Later

Chapter 4
Self-Test

For items 1-3, figure the extra cost to buy on credit. (See pages 84-90.)

1. You can buy a stereo for $325.00 cash, or you can buy it on credit for $20.00 per month for 24 months. How much extra to buy on credit?

2. Living room furniture costs $1200 in cash. It can also be purchased on credit for $100 per month for 18 months. How much more to buy on credit?

3. Maria wants a new stove which costs $735.50. She can also buy it on credit for $50.00 a month for 18 months. How much more will she pay if she buys the stove on credit?

For items 4-6, figure the amount of the down payment. Round your answers to the nearest cent. (See pages 91-93.)

4. $782.75 (20% down)

5. $2440.00 (¼ down)

6. $1687.25 (15% down)

For items 7-9, solve the problems. (See pages 93-97.)

7. On August 15 you receive a bill for T.V. repairs. The bill is due September 10. How many days do you have to pay it?

8. On July 26, you receive a water bill. The payment is due August 15. How many days do you have to pay it?

9. You receive a bill from your doctor on April 3. You must pay it by May 20. How many days do you have to pay it?

For items 10-12. figure the finance charge on the unpaid balance of each bill. Assume you are paying the minimum amount due. Round your answers to the nearest cent, if necessary. (See pages 97-102.)

10.	Finance Rate	Minimum Amount Due	Balance
	1.5%	$10.00	$562.25

11. Finance Minimum
    Rate   Amount Due   Balance

    2.0% $25.00 $1,645.00

12. Finance Minimum
    Rate   Amount Due   Balance

    1.2% $12.50 $96.75

For items 13-15, figure the monthly payment for each of the long term loans. Round to the nearest cent if necessary. (See pages 102-106.)

13. $25,000 at 11% for 20 years.

14. $975 at 8% for 2 years.

15. $10,520 at 9% for 5 years.

CHAPTER

MAKING ENDS MEET

USING BASIC MATH SKILLS TO SOLVE PROBLEMS RELATED TO BUDGETING.

KEY WORDS:

1. **Budget:** a record of how much money you take home and how much you plan spend for specific items.
2. **Fixed Expenses:** on a budget, the expenses that are necessary and cannot be cut.
3. **Flexible Expenses:** on a budget, the expenses that you can reduce in size or cut out completely, if necessary.
4. **Receipts:** a sales record given to you by a business, showing what you bought and how much you paid.
5. **Rent:** the money you pay to a landlord for housing.
6. **Utilities:** services such as electricity, gas, and water, provided at a charge to homes and apartments.

SKILL: Figuring the total monthly cost of housing (*rent* and *utilities*).

Ranzo has decided it is time for him to find a place of his own, so he moves into an apartment which rents for $210 a month. He thinks that this amount of rent is perfect for him, because that is just what he can afford.

Unfortunately, he did not know that he would need extra money to pay for his *utilities.* In the apartment he shared with Anja and Miro, the utilities were *included* in the rent, but his new rent of $210 does *not* include utilities.

He has just received gas and electric bills for $55. Ranzo does not know what to do, because he cannot afford to pay the $55, so he asks Anja and Miro over to help him decide what to do.

√ 1.

EXPENSES	
Rent	$150.00
Gas	35.18
Water	15.62
Electric	27.35
Total	

√ 2.

EXPENSES	
Gas	$ 22.55
Rent	215.00
Water	16.45
Electric	38.50
Total	

3.

EXPENSES	
Water	$ 8.75
Gas	22.58
Electric	25.20
Rent	253.76
Total	

4.

EXPENSES	
Rent	$164.86
Gas	43.90
Water	5.19
Electric	35.50
Total	

5.

EXPENSES	
Water	$ 12.65
Gas	27.53
Electric	26.78
Rent	138.75
Total	

6.

EXPENSES	
Electric	$ 37.49
Rent	155.54
Water	10.85
Gas	18.46
Total	

7.

EXPENSES	
Water	$ 8.68
Gas	22.20
Rent	95.26
Electric	26.25
Total	

8.

EXPENSES	
Electric	$ 20.59
Rent	350.45
Gas	36.56
Water	6.75
Total	

9.

EXPENSES	
Water	$ 5.48
Rent	167.50
Gas	20.17
Electric	18.95
Total	

Here are some additional practice problems. Figure the total housing cost a person would have to pay for each apartment listed below.

1.

Rent	$100.00
Gas	12.79
Electric	31.44
Water	5.77

2.

Water	$ 11.21
Gas	56.01
Electric	19.44
Rent	225.00

3.

Electric	$ 35.16
Gas	9.44
Rent	162.57
Water	3.22

4.

Water	$ 21.44
Electric	47.11
Gas	9.67
Rent	125.05

5.

Rent	$ 95.58
Gas	10.40
Water	3.44
Electric	23.62

6.

Gas	$ 14.49
Water	4.94
Rent	133.85
Electric	10.14

7.

Gas	$ 39.05
Electric	27.57
Rent	356.43
Water	83.66

8.

Rent	$178.35
Water	11.92
Gas	23.19
Electric	12.51

9.

Electric	$ 56.77
Gas	14.96
Water	6.09
Rent	270.11

Making Ends Meet

Anja tells Ranzo that he should learn to keep a *budget.* She explains that a *budget* is a record of how much you *earn* each month and how much you expect to *spend* each month.

MONTHLY EXPENSES	
Earnings	**Expenses**

Under "Earnings" list the money you earn each month. At the bottom, you *add* the amounts to get "*Total Monthly Earnings.*" Under "Expenses", list the money you expect to spend each month. At the bottom, you *add* the amounts to get "*Total Monthly Expenses.*"

Earnings		**Expenses**	
Pay (Harry's Used Cars)	$ 42.50	Help with the Rent	$ 10.00
Mowing Lawns	15.60	Getting around	10.00
		Savings	20.00
		Spending money	18.10
Total Monthly Earnings	$ 58.10	Total Monthly Expenses	$ 58.10

On a budget, your total earnings should match your total expenses.

SAMPLE:

Monthly Expenses

May	$ 20.60
June	23.92
July	18.41
August	21.63
September	20.14

Add to get total

$ 20.60
23.92
18.41
21.63
20.14
―――
$104.70

Divide by number of months to get average monthly costs.

$ 20.94
5) $104.70
   10
   ―
    4
    0
   ――
   47
   45
   ――
    20
    20

Average Monthly Costs = $20.94

For each list of the following receipts, figure the average monthly costs. (Round your answers to the nearest cent)

√ 1.

Groceries	
May	$ 75.06
June	70.93
July	80.41
August	68.14
September	90.32
Average _____	

√ 2.

Telephone	
May	$ 8.63
June	12.41
July	10.58
August	10.54
September	11.68
October	9.62
Average _____	

3.

Laundry	
June	$ 8.44
July	6.32
August	5.19
September	12.46
Average _____	

4.

Gas For Car	
May	$ 15.63
June	18.42
July	20.06
August	18.73
September	19.41
October	22.18
Average _____	

5.

Clothing	
May	$ 20.16
June	15.82
July	3.41
August	25.19
September	18.64
Average _____	

6.

Lunch At Work	
May	$ 20.00
June	25.16
July	18.63
August	30.04
September	11.51
October	7.58
Average _____	

7.

Dry Cleaning	
May	$ 6.01
June	7.38
July	5.42
August	10.19
Average _____	

8.

Transportation	
May	$ 5.63
June	3.61
July	4.92
August	8.16
September	3.98
Average _____	

9.

Telephone	
May	$ 20.08
June	31.75
July	25.16
August	18.41
Average _____	

10.

Water Bills	
September	$ 15.64
October	12.91
November	13.84
December	16.58
January	12.93
Average _____	

11.

Clothing	
April	$ 15.85
May	20.94
June	13.68
July	25.73
August	18.62
September	19.21
Average _____	

12.

Entertainment	
March	$ 35.62
April	40.84
May	38.27
June	42.63
Average _____	

13.

Groceries	
November	$ 95.18
December	101.62
January	86.14
February	97.62
Average _____	

14.

Electric Bills	
February	$ 25.64
March	18.79
April	19.53
May	28.63
June	27.94
Average _____	

15.

Lunch	
March	$ 10.15
April	9.82
May	10.86
Average _____	

16.

Books & Magazines	
November	$17.63
December	12.05
January	19.62
February	11.18
Average _____	

17.

Record Albums	
October	$ 15.63
November	12.82
December	11.17
January	14.08
Average _____	

18.

Gas Bills	
August	$ 63.00
September	58.19
October	73.84
November	62.10
December	65.73
Average _____	

For more practice in figuring the average monthly cost for budget expenses, work the following problems. Round your answers to the nearest cent when necessary.

1.

Entertainment	
June	$ 15.26
July	12.40
August	11.96
September	19.47
Average _____	

2.

Movies	
March	$ 8.75
April	6.40
May	7.95
June	10.80
Average _____	

3.

Yard & Garden	
April	$ 27.91
May	59.62
June	41.14
July	11.71
August	18.30
Average _____	

Making Ends Meet

4.

Lunch	
December	$ 16.23
January	9.27
February	17.67
March	19.71
April	10.62
Average	

5.

Gas Bills	
November	$ 51.19
December	63.26
January	72.38
Average	

6.

Dentist	
May	$ 26.25
July	19.64
September	27.11
December	36.80
Average	

7.

Baby Sitter	
May	$ 17.15
June	15.95
July	21.00
August	19.75
September	11.20
October	12.85
Average	

8.

Record Albums	
August	$ 27.54
September	15.68
October	16.84
November	20.45
Average	

9.

Clothing	
September	$ 26.45
October	19.77
November	28.86
December	31.19
Average	

10.

Restaurants	
February	$ 47.31
March	39.68
April	55.88
May	27.73
Average	

11.

Telephone	
June	$ 28.14
July	17.86
August	23.05
September	31.27
October	28.90
Average	

12.

House Repairs	
December	$ 39.64
January	39.11
February	47.22
Average	

13.

Doctor	
May	$ 75.21
August	38.98
January	57.61
February	43.46
Average	

14.

Electric Bills	
June	$ 18.41
July	21.60
August	27.14
September	23.01
October	15.31
November	18.69
Average	

15.

Water Bill	
January	$ 3.61
February	4.14
March	8.93
April	6.26
Average	

16. Groceries			17. Transportation			18. Books	

16.

Groceries

June	$ 97.82
July	105.46
August	79.28
September	64.13

Average _____

17.

Transportation

November	$ 5.15
December	6.40
January	4.80
February	4.90
March	6.25

Average _____

18.

Books

June	$ 13.16
July	18.65
August	19.91
September	11.80

Average _____

SKILL: Figuring the total amount needed to meet a monthly budget.

Ranzo has learned that total expected monthly expenses should match total monthly earnings. He has also learned what can happen if you *spend* more than you *make.*

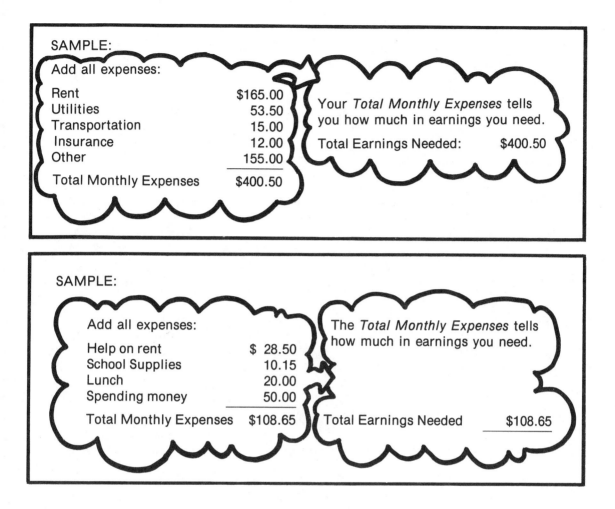

SAMPLE:

Add all expenses:

Rent	$165.00
Utilities	53.50
Transportation	15.00
Insurance	12.00
Other	155.00
Total Monthly Expenses	$400.50

Your *Total Monthly Expenses* tells you how much in earnings you need.

Total Earnings Needed: $400.50

SAMPLE:

Add all expenses:

Help on rent	$ 28.50
School Supplies	10.15
Lunch	20.00
Spending money	50.00
Total Monthly Expenses	$108.65

The *Total Monthly Expenses* tells how much in earnings you need.

Total Earnings Needed $108.65

Figure the total monthly earnings you would need to meet the budget expenses in the following lists.

√ 1.

EXPENSES	
Rent	$165.00
Utilities	53.50
Transportation	15.00
Insurance	12.00
Other	155.00
Total Expenses	

Total Earnings Needed____

√ 2.

EXPENSES	
Rent	$200.15
Utilities	75.00
Entertainment	100.00
Groceries	85.00
Other	105.00
Savings	50.00
Total Expenses	

Total Earnings Needed____

3.

EXPENSES	
Help on Rent	$ 50.00
Help on Utilities	15.00
Lunch	25.00
Clothing	22.00
Books & Records	15.00
Total Expenses	

Total Earnings Needed____

4.

EXPENSES	
Savings	$ 35.00
Rent	185.00
Utilities	63.00
Transportation	15.00
Groceries	65.00
Other	150.00
Total Expenses	

Total Earnings Needed____

5.

EXPENSES	
Rent	$225.30
Utilities	85.60
Groceries	105.00
Insurance	15.28
Clothing	30.00
Other	150.00
Total Expenses	

Total Earnings Needed____

6.

EXPENSES	
Help on Rent	$ 15.50
Snacks	30.00
Clothing	12.75
Magazines	3.00
Total Expenses	

Total Earnings Needed____

7.

EXPENSES	
Savings	$200.00
Rent	315.75
Utilities	81.00
Groceries	115.00
Other	225.00
Total Expenses	

Total Earnings Needed____

8.

EXPENSES	
Rent	$195.85
Utilities	85.60
Transportation	25.00
Insurance	18.35
Other	160.00
Total Expenses	

Total Earnings Needed____

9.

EXPENSES	
Rent	$200.15
Utilities	75.00
Groceries	95.50
Insurance	12.15
Savings	150.00
Other	160.00
Total Expenses	

Total Earnings Needed____

For more practice, figure the total monthly earnings you would need to meet the expected budget expenses in the following lists.

1.

EXPENSES	
Car	$ 78.00
Groceries	45.00
Insurance	87.58
Utilities	43.60
Books	18.00
Other	20.00
Total Earnings Needed ____	

2.

EXPENSES	
Insurance	$123.88
Books	25.00
Snacks	18.00
Rent	175.50
Other	25.00
Total Earnings Needed ____	

3.

EXPENSES	
Savings	$150.00
Rent	225.00
Utilities	87.40
Groceries	73.00
Other	100.00
Total Earnings Needed ____	

4.

EXPENSES	
Transportation	$ 80.35
Groceries	67.50
Clothing	25.00
Savings	75.00
Other	50.00

Total Earnings
Needed _____

5.

EXPENSES	
Other	$ 65.00
Rent	115.25
Utilities	38.50
Savings	50.00

Total Earnings
Needed _____

6.

EXPENSES	
Clothing	$ 38.85
Rent	155.00
Savings	65.00
Insurance	82.53
Utilities	56.00
Other	80.00

Total Earnings
Needed _____

WHAT HAPPENS IF THE EXPENSES ARE MORE THAN THE EARNINGS?

THEN YOU HAVE TO MAKE A BETTER BUDGET BY CUTTING IT.

WHEN YOU CUT A BUDGET, YOU CHECK IT TO SEE WHICH EXPENSES CAN BE REDUCED OR TAKEN OUT COMPLETELY.

OF COURSE, THERE ARE SOME EXPENSES THAT YOU CAN'T CUT. THESE ARE CALLED FIXED EXPENSES.

FIXED EXPENSES ARE ALSO THOSE THAT YOU KNOW ABOUT HOW MUCH THEY'LL COST EACH MONTH.

THERE ARE SOME THINGS THAT CAN BE CUT FROM A BUDGET.

FIXED EXPENSES

Rent
Utilities
Insurance
Transportation

FLEXIBLE EXPENSES

Movies
Record Albums
Magazines
Snacks
Roller Skating

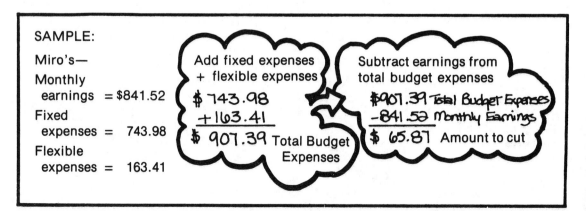

SAMPLE:

Miro's—
Monthly
  earnings = $841.52
Fixed
  expenses =   743.98
Flexible
  expenses =   163.41

Add fixed expenses + flexible expenses

$ 743.98
+163.41
$ 907.39 Total Budget Expenses

Subtract earnings from total budget expenses

$907.39 Total Budget Expenses
−841.52 Monthly Earnings
$ 65.87 Amount to cut

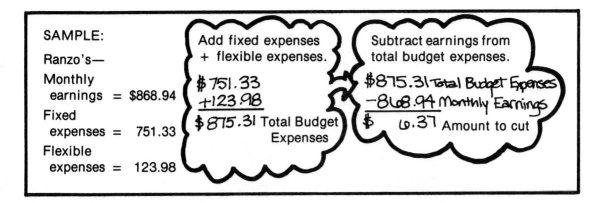

SAMPLE:

Ranzo's—

Monthly earnings = $868.94

Fixed expenses = 751.33

Flexible expenses = 123.98

Add fixed expenses + flexible expenses.

$751.33
+123.98
$875.31 Total Budget Expenses

Subtract earnings from total budget expenses.

$875.31 Total Budget Expenses
−868.94 Monthly Earnings
$ 6.37 Amount to cut

See if you can cut the following budget. Go over each expense and decide if it is "fixed" or "flexible." Then, cut the amounts of flexible expenses (or take them out completely) so that the total monthly earnings matches exactly the total monthly expenses. When you have matched earnings and expenses, prepare a new budget.

Earnings		Expenses	
Paycheck	$398.00	Rent & Utilities	$155.00
		Books	12.50
		Transportation (to and from work)	20.00
		Insurance Bill	15.50
		Water Bill	10.50
		Savings	100.00
		Groceries	85.00
		Spending Money	53.50
Total Earnings	$398.00	Total Expenses	$452.00

$ 285 Fixed Expense
+100 Savings
$ 385

Total earnings:	$473.50
Fixed Exp. + Savings:	385.00
Flexible Expenses	$ 88.50

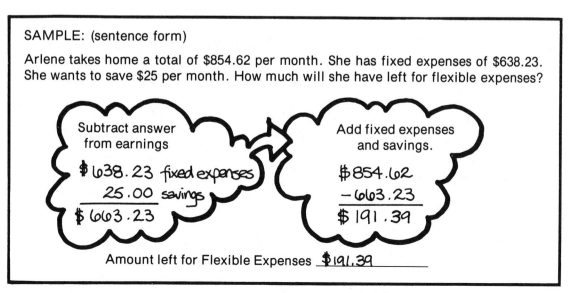

SAMPLE: (sentence form)

Arlene takes home a total of $854.62 per month. She has fixed expenses of $638.23. She wants to save $25 per month. How much will she have left for flexible expenses?

Subtract answer from earnings

$ 638.23 fixed expenses
  25.00 savings
$ 663.23

Add fixed expenses and savings.

$854.62
−663.23
$ 191.39

Amount left for Flexible Expenses $191.39

SAMPLE: (budget form)

What is the amount left for flexible expenses in this budget?

BUDGET

Earnings	Expenses	
Pay $563.21	Rent	$185.00
	Utilities	63.00
Fixed { Insurance	21.00
	Doctor's Bill	35.00
	Savings	50.00
	Flexible {	
Total $563.21	Total	$563.21

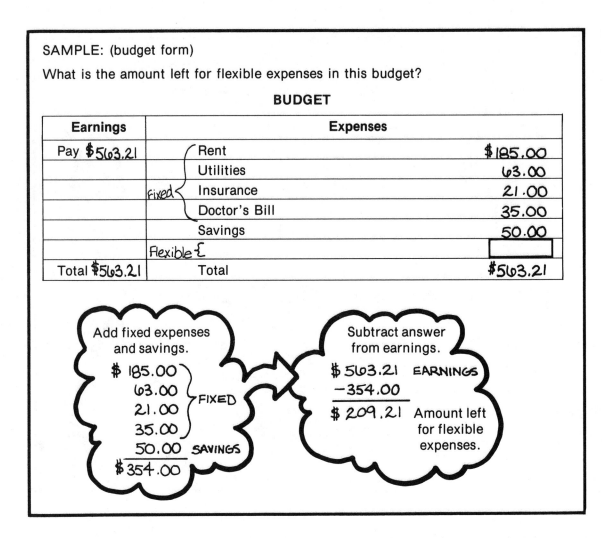

Add fixed expenses and savings.

$ 185.00 ⎱
63.00 ⎰ FIXED
21.00
35.00 ⎰
50.00 SAVINGS
$354.00

Subtract answer from earnings.

$ 563.21 EARNINGS
−354.00
$ 209.21 Amount left for flexible expenses.

Solve each of the following budget problems. (Round to nearest cent when necessary.)

√ 1. Allen Barnes takes home $1,056.69 each month. He wants to save 15 percent of this. He has fixed expenses of $701.83. How much can he budget for flexible expenses?

2. Hans Gurin has fixed expenses of $345.89 each month. He wants to save $60.50 each month from his take-home pay. His take-home pay is $843.78 each month. How much can he budget for flexible expenses?

3. Sara Berns wants to save 20 percent of her monthly take-home pay of $543.52. She has fixed expenses of $225.63. How much can she budget for flexible expenses?

Making Ends Meet

√ 4. Figure the amount left in this budget for flexible expenses.

Earnings		Expenses		
Pay	$741.68		Savings	$ 95.00
		Fixed	Rent	200.00
			Utilities	85.00
		Flexible		
Total	$741.68	Total Expenses		$741.68

5. Figure the amount left in this budget for flexible expenses.

Earnings		Expenses		
Pay	$263.41	Fixed	Help with Rent	$ 25.00
			Savings	150.00
		Flexible		
Total	$263.41	Total Expenses		$263.41

6. Figure the amount left in this budget for flexible expenses.

Earnings		Expenses		
Pay	$953.84		Rent	$250.00
		Fixed	Utilities	56.00
			Insurance	85.00
			Transportation	25.00
			Savings	125.00
		Flexible		
Total	$953.84	Total Expenses		$953.84

For additional practice with budgets, solve the following problems. Round to the nearest cent when necessary.

1. Margaret Miller would like to save $100 each month from her take-home pay of $608.71. She has fixed expenses of $319.60. How much can she allow for flexible expenses?

2. Figure the amount in this budget for flexible expenses.

Earnings		Expenses		
Pay	$428.96	Fixed	Groceries	$125.00
			Rent	160.00
			Books	20.00
			Transportation	35.00
		Flexible		
Total	$428.96	Total		$428.96

3. Gloria Redman has fixed expenses each month of $378.52. She takes home $791.00 each month. If she saves 15% of her take home pay, how much can she budget for flexible expenses?

4. Figure the amount left for flexible expenses in this budget.

Earnings		Expenses		
Pay	$626.48	Fixed	Rent	$250.00
			Utilities	62.00
			Insurance	26.00
			Clothing	40.00
			Savings	50.00
		Flexible		
Total	$626.48	Total		$626.48

5. Carlos Riojas wants to save $85.00 from his monthly take-home pay of $561.23. If he has fixed expenses of $283.66, how much can he budget for flexible expenses?

6. Figure the amount left for flexible expenses in this budget.

Earnings		Expenses		
Pay	$798.21	Fixed	Rent	$300.00
			Groceries	85.00
			Insurance	23.57
			Savings	40.00
		Flexible		
Total	$798.21	Total		$798.21

7. Inez Smithers has fixed expenses of $572.28 each month. If her take home pay is $962.47 and she saves $200.00 each month, how much can she allow for flexible expenses?

Making Ends Meet

8. Figure the amount left for flexible expenses in this budget.

Earnings		Expenses		
Pay	$649.22	*Fixed*	Transportation	$ 80.00
			Rent	225.00
			Groceries	120.00
			Savings	100.00
			Utilities	40.00
		Flexible		
Total	$649.22	Total		$649.22

SKILL: Figuring the money left over after budgeting for expenses.

SAMPLE:

Earnings		Expenses	
$ 659.57		Rent	$ 150.00
		Utilities	63.00
		Transportation	25.50
		Clothing	18.00
		Groceries	95.00
		Other Expenses	115.00
Total Earnings	$659.57	Total Expenses	$ 466.50

For each budget below, figure the money left after meeting the listed expenses. Then, decide what could be done with the left-over earnings. Choose the activity that comes closest to, without going over, the amount of left-over earnings.

Making Ends Meet

√ 1.

Earnings		Expenses	
Pay	$215.64	Help with Rent	$ 25.50
		School Expenses	8.70
		Entertainment	15.00
		Savings	85.00
Total Earnings	$215.64	Total Expenses	

A. Buy a $200 savings bond
C. Put another $150 into savings
B. Buy a $20 pair of track shoes
D. Buy a $60 watch

2.

Earnings		Expenses	
Pay	$618.49	Rent	$125.00
		Transportation	22.00
		Groceries	65.50
		Utilities	25.30
		Other	100.00
		Spending Money	175.00
Total	$618.49	Total	

A. Buy a $95 TV set
C. Buy $100 worth of clothing
B. Take a vacation costing $200
D. Put $85 into a savings account

3.

Earnings		Expenses	
Pay	$563.94	Rent	$150.00
		Transportation	15.50
		Groceries	85.00
		Utilities	53.00
		Entertainment	25.00
		Spending Money	100.00
Total	$563.94	Total	

A. Buy a $120 radio
C. Buy a $140 piece of jewelry.
B. Buy $150 worth of shoes and ties
D. Put $115 into a savings account.

4.

Earnings		Expenses	
Pay	$493.21	Rent	$136.50
		Utilities	37.40
		Groceries	68.75
		Insurance	10.52
		Other	56.20
		Spending Money	150.00
Total	$493.21	Total	

A. Put $50 into savings   B. Buy a $15 dinner at a fancy restaurant
C. Buy $40 worth of books   D. Buy record albums worth $12.50

For more practice, use the following budgets to figure the money left after meeting the listed expenses. Then decide what you might do with the left-over earnings from the four things listed below the budget. Choose the activity which comes closest to, without going over, the amount of your left-over earnings.

1.

Earnings		Expenses	
Pay	$503.64	Rent	$115.00
		Utilities	40.00
		Transportation	60.00
		Entertainment	30.00
		Groceries	85.00
		Spending Money	115.00
Total	$503.64	Total Expenses	

A. Buy a $14 set of records   C. Buy $55 worth of clothing
B. Buy a $45 watch   D. Put $100 into a savings account

2.

Earnings		Expenses	
Pay	$516.98	Rent	$ 99.50
		Utilities	35.00
		Transportation	16.00
		Spending Money	125.00
		Groceries	90.00
		Other Expenses	50.00
Total	$516.98	Total Expenses	

A. Buy a $115 record player
B. Buy $200 worth of clothing
C. Take a vacation costing $100
D. Put $150 into a savings account

3.

Earnings		Expenses	
Pay	$863.98	Rent	$125.00
		Utilities	40.00
		Transportation	15.00
		Insurance	35.15
		Groceries	60.00
		Spending Money	125.00
Total	$863.98	Total Expenses	

A. Buy $75 worth of slacks
B. Buy a $600 tape recorder
C. Take a vacation costing $250
D. Put $300 into a savings account

4.

Earnings		Expenses	
Pay	$306.41	Help with Rent	$ 50.00
		Lunches at School	35.00
		Transportation	30.00
		Clothing	25.00
		Savings	50.00
		Savings	50.00
Total	$306.41	Total Expenses	

A. Buy a $120 radio
B. Put $200 into a savings account
C. Buy a $140 piece of jewelry
D. Buy a $50 savings bond

5.

Earnings		Expenses	
Pay	$553.98	Rent	$165.50
		Utilities	45.75
		Insurance	12.14
		Spending Money	125.00
		Groceries	90.00
Total	$553.98	Total Expenses	

A. Buy a $100 pair of tires
B. Put $250 into a savings account
C. Buy a $65 record player
D. Buy a $20 hat and a $50 pair of shoes

6.

Earnings		Expenses	
Pay	$601.47	Rent	$215.25
		Utilities	38.00
		Insurance	5.98
		Other expenses	200.00
		Groceries	75.00
Total	$601.47	Total Expenses	

A. Buy $50 worth of books
B. Take a vacation costing $300
C. Put $25 into a savings account
D. Buy $80 worth of records.

Chapter 5
Self-Test

For items 1-3, figure the average monthly cost of each expense. (See pages 114-118.)

1.

Transportation	
September	$21.75
October	16.34
November	23.48
December	19.23
January	28.17

2.

Groceries	
March	$102.78
April	98.42
May	79.84
June	120.73
July	110.72
August	117.27

3.

Gas	
January	$41.26
February	39.23
March	45.62
April	37.27
May	44.83

For items 4-6, figure the total housing costs. (See pages 110-113.)

4.

Water	$ 10.75
Rent	165.00
Gas	86.24
Electric	72.41

5.

Rent	$175.00
Water	12.72
Gas	73.81
Electric	52.17

6.

Rent	$210.00
Gas	56.48
Electric	37.81
Water	15.56

For items 7-9, figure the total earnings needed to meet each budget. (See pages 118-123.)

7.

Expenses	
Rent	$250.00
Utilities	87.92
Savings	50.00
Groceries	125.63
Other	150.75

8.

Expenses	
Rent	$275.00
Utilities	75.42
Insurance	21.75
Groceries	98.21
Spending Money	120.00

9.

Expenses	
Rent	$215.00
Clothing	73.25
Savings	75.00
Transportation	16.35
Groceries	110.30
Insurance	32.48

For items 10-12, solve each problem. (See pages 124-129.)

10. Bruce wants to save $75.50 out of his monthly take-home pay of $784.63. He has fixed expenses of $349.35. How much will he have left for flexible expenses?

11. Nadine takes home $954.00 a month. She want to save 10% of this. She has fixed expenses of $365.00. How much will she have left for flexible expenses?

12. Ursula has a monthly take-home pay of $820.75. She has fixed expenses of $315.85 and wants to save $30.00 per month. How much will she have left for flexible expenses?

For items 13-15, figure the money left over after budgeting for listed expenses. (See pages 129-132.)

13.

Earnings		Expenses	
Pay	$875.00	Rent	$195.00
		Insurance	25.79
Total	$875.00	Utilities	80.73
		Savings	85.00

14.

Earnings		Expenses	
Pay	$998.75	Rent	$250.00
		Groceries	112.93
		Utilities	49.87
Total	$998.75	Savings	100.00

15.

Earnings		Expenses	
Pay	$703.65	Rent	$200.00
		Clothing	70.50
		Groceries	89.60
Total	$703.65	Utilities	42.65
		Savings	25.00

Making Ends Meet

BUYING WISELY

USING BASIC MATH SKILLS TO SOLVE PROBLEMS RELATED TO BEING A WISE CONSUMER.

KEY WORDS:

1. **Buying in Quantity:** buying more of a product to save money.

2. **Kilowatt:** a unit for measuring electrical power. A kilowatt equals 1000 watts.

3. **Kilowatt Hour:** a way to measure your usage of electricity. Electric companies charge you for each kilowatt hour you use. A kilowatt hour is the amount of electric power it takes to light ten 100-watt light bulbs for one hour.

4. **KWH:** an abbreviation for ''kilowatt hour.''

5. **Out of State Long Distance Phone Calls:** calls you make on the phone to a person or business outside your state.

6. **Sample Rate Chart:** a chart showing how much it costs to call different cities from your home town.

7. **Unit Price:** the price of a product per unit; for example, per ounce or per pound. By comparing the unit prices of things you buy, you can find the least expensive product.

8. **Watt:** a unit for measuring electrical power.

SKILL: Figuring the cost for electricity you use at home.

The three Arithmians have purchased almost every kind of electrical appliance available in America. The problem is, they usually run everything all at once. Ranzo loves to play the radio and T.V. while vacuuming. They really never bother to turn off lights when they don't need them. Miro loves to run the air conditioner when a fan may do just as much good.

All this waste of electricity catches up to them when they begin receiving huge electric bills. Anja decides to check into where they are going wrong and learns some important information.

SAMPLE:

COMMUNITY ELECTRIC COMPANY

Rate	KWH Used	Amount Due
$.09/KWH	750	$67.50

To find the amount you owe for electricity,
multiply KWH (kilowatt hours) used by the rate.

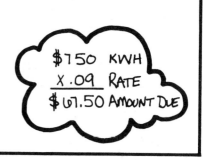

$750 KWH
X .09 RATE
$67.50 AMOUNT DUE

Miro, Anja, and Ranzo discuss ways they can cut down on the number of "kilowatt units" they use. They find their air conditioner uses 1000 watts, which is ten times the energy used for a 100 watt lightbulb.

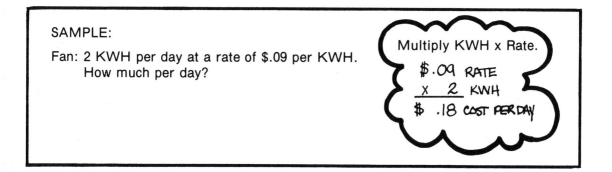

SAMPLE:

Fan: 2 KWH per day at a rate of $.09 per KWH.
How much per day?

Multiply KWH x Rate.

$.09 RATE
x 2 KWH
$ .18 COST PER DAY

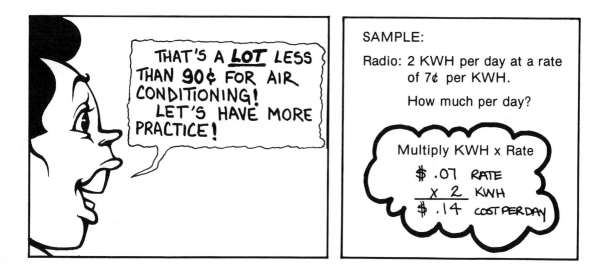

THAT'S A **LOT** LESS THAN 90¢ FOR AIR CONDITIONING! LET'S HAVE MORE PRACTICE!

SAMPLE:

Radio: 2 KWH per day at a rate of 7¢ per KWH.

How much per day?

Multiply KWH x Rate

$ .07 RATE
x 2 KWH
$ .14 COST PER DAY

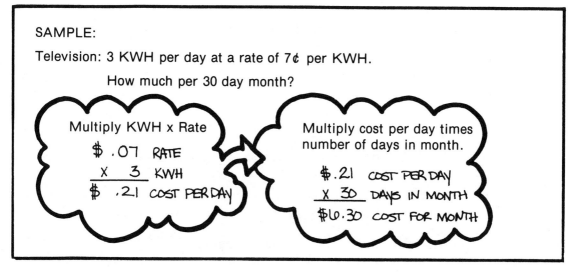

SAMPLE:

Television: 3 KWH per day at a rate of 7¢ per KWH.

How much per 30 day month?

Multiply KWH x Rate

$ .07 RATE
x 3 KWH
$ .21 COST PER DAY

Multiply cost per day times number of days in month.

$.21 COST PER DAY
x 30 DAYS IN MONTH
$6.30 COST FOR MONTH

Now solve these problems. (Round your answers to the nearest cent when necessary.)

√ 1. A washing machine uses 5 KWH each time it is used. The cost is 8¢ per KWH. How much does it cost each time the washing machine is used?

√ 2. A refrigerator uses 12 KWH per day, at a rate of 6.5¢ per KWH. What is the cost per day for the refrigerator?

3. A freezer uses 6.4 KWH per day. The rate is 6.5¢ per KWH. How much does it cost per day for the freezer?

4. A toaster uses 1.1 KWH in a week. The cost is 8¢ per KWH. What is the weekly cost of using the toaster?

5. In a month, Miro's crockpot uses 3 KWH. At a rate of 8.5 cents per KWH, what is the monthly cost?

6. A water heater uses 13.4 KWH in an afternoon. The cost is 4.5¢ per KWH. What is the total cost for one afternoon's use?

7. A refrigerator-freezer uses about 1,500 KWH in a year. The cost is 9¢ per KWH. What is the total cost for 1 year?

8. Anja's electric blanket uses about 150 KWH in a year. Her air conditioner uses about 860 KWH in a year. The rate for each is 8.5¢ per KWH. What is the total cost for both appliances for one year?

9. A T.V. uses about 1 KWH per day. At a rate of 9¢ per KWH, what is the monthly cost of watching T.V.? (Use 30 days as a month.)

10. Ranzo's oven uses 4 KWH per day. At a rate of 6.5¢ per KWH, what does the oven cost in electricity each day?

11. A big freezer uses about 42 KWH in a week. The rate is $.07 per KWH. How much does it cost to run a large freezer for a week?

For more practice, solve the following problems. Round your answers to the nearest cent when necessary.

1. The fan on the Arithmians' furnace uses 1 KWH every hour of use. At a cost of 9 cents per KWH, what is the cost per day when the fan runs 8 hours each day?

2. Ranzo's clothes washer used 25 KWH last month. His dryer used 32 KWH. At a rate of 7 cents per KWH, how much did it cost Ranzo to run his washer and dryer last month?

3. A 3 ton air conditioner uses 840 KWH in a week. The rate is 6 cents per KWH. How much does it cost to run the air conditioner each week?

4. The Arithmians' refrigerator uses 6.1 KWH per day. Their dishwasher uses 3.5 KWH per day. At a rate of 7.5 cents per KWH, how much does it cost them every day to use these two appliances?

5. Every time Anja uses her hair dryer, it consumes about 2 KWH. At a rate of 9 cents per KWH, about how much does it cost Anja to blow-dry her hair 7 times a week?

6. Miro's electric frying pan uses about 1.5 KWH per hour of use. His electric rate is 8 cents per KWH. How much does it cost Miro to use the frying pan for one-half hour?

> SKILL: Figuring the charge for making out of state long distance phone calls.

Learning how much then can save on their electric bill, the Arithmians decide that they may be able to save on all their utilities, such as the telephone. Anja checks into it and finds their biggest savings could be on *out of state long distance phone calls,* if they remember these three things:
1. *Make the calls yourself.* (If the operator helps, you pay more.)
2. *Control how long you talk.* (The longer you talk, the more you pay.)
3. *Call, when possible, at the time of the lowest rate.* (The rate you pay depends on the time of day you make your call.)

The chart shown below lists cities you might call and the rates for calling these cities at different times or days.

From River City to:	Weekday Each		Evening Each		Night/Weekend Each	
	First Minute	Additional Minute	First Minute	Additional Minute	First Minute	Additional Minute
Atlanta	.50	.34	.32	.23	.20	.14
Boston	.52	.36	.33	.24	.20	.15
Chicago	.48	.34	.31	.23	.19	.14
Dallas	.50	.34	.32	.23	.20	.14
Denver	.50	.34	.32	.23	.20	.14
Los Angeles	.52	.36	.33	.24	.20	.15
Mpls.-St. Paul	.46	.32	.29	.21	.18	.13
New Orleans	.50	.34	.32	.23	.20	.14
New York	.52	.36	.33	.24	.20	.15
Omaha	.43	.28	.27	.19	.17	.12
San Francisco	.52	.36	.33	.24	.20	.15
Sioux Falls	.46	.32	.29	.21	.18	.13

Weekday:
8 AM - 5 PM,
Monday through Friday.

Evening:
5 PM - 11 PM,
Sunday through Friday.

Night/Weekend:
11 PM - 8 AM, any day;
All day Saturday:
8 AM - 5 PM, Sunday

SAMPLE: Mr. Carey called a friend in San Francisco on a Saturday night. They talked for 25 minutes. At the weekend rate, how much did the call cost?

Find the rate for calling San Francisco on the weekend (see chart).

	Week-day	Even-ing	Night/ Week-end
San Francisco			.20/.15

Add the charges for the 1st minute and the total charges for additional minutes.

$ .20 (1ST MINUTE)
+3.60 (15¢ X 24 MINUTES)
$3.80 TOTAL COST OF CALL

SAMPLE: Mrs. Blake called Dallas during the day on Tuesday. She talked 28 minutes. How much did the call cost?

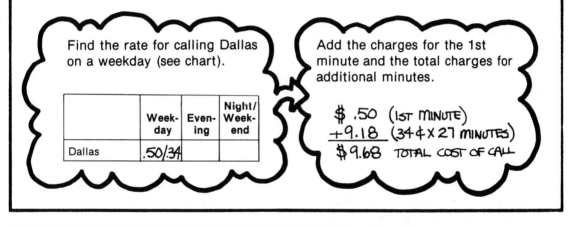

Find the rate for calling Dallas on a weekday (see chart).

	Week-day	Even-ing	Night/Week-end
Dallas	.50/.34		

Add the charges for the 1st minute and the total charges for additional minutes.

$ .50 (1st MINUTE)
+9.18 (34¢ × 27 MINUTES)
$9.68 TOTAL COST OF CALL

THAT'S IT! SEE HOW MUCH WE CAN SAVE BY KNOWING HOW TO FIGURE OUT THESE CHARGES?

I NEVER KNEW THERE IS SUCH A BIG DIFFERENCE IN RATES FROM ONE TIME TO ANOTHER, BUT I'M SURE I'LL REMEMBER NOW!

See if you can solve the following problems. Use the same rate chart the Arithmians used on page 144.

1. On Sunday morning, Carl called the President, who was visiting Atlanta. He talked to

the President's secretary for 15 minutes. (The President was busy.) How much did the call cost?

√ 2. At 7 p.m. Monday, Rosa phoned the radio station QXIR talk show in Boston. She was on the line for 13 minutes. How much did the call cost?

3. Frank wanted to order a skateboard from a company in Los Angeles. He called during the day and talked for 6 minutes. How much did the call cost?

4. On Wednesday evening Joel called Chicago to see if it was raining there. He talked to a TV weather forecaster for two minutes. How much did the call cost?

5. On Friday night at 11:36, Jane called Sioux Falls to see if anybody lived there. Somebody did. They talked for 43 minutes. How much did the call cost?

6. Sandy called the Ace Comb Company in Dallas during the day on Tuesday. She wanted to order a 50 cent comb. She talked for 27 minutes. How much did the call cost?

For more practice in figuring telephone rates, solve these problems. Use the rate chart on page 144.

1. Ken called Denver to see if it was snowing there. He called at 8 o'clock on a Thursday evening. He talked with a radio weather forecaster for seven minutes. How much did the call cost?

2. On Saturday morning, Owen called an insurance company in Omaha. The office was closed but Owen talked with the company janitor for 12 minutes. How much did the call cost?

3. Ruth heard that New York City was called "The Big Apple." She called the New York City library at 3 p.m. on Wednesday to ask why. She talked with a librarian for 1 minute. How much did the call cost her?

4. At 8:30 Thursday morning, Bill called the New Orleans Police Department to ask whatever happened to *Old* Orleans. He talked with a policeman for 3 minutes. How much did the call cost?

5. Robin woke up at 3 a.m. Wednesday with nothing to do. She called the Minneapolis Fire Department. She talked with a fire fighter for 63 minutes. How much did the call cost her?

6. Betsy once called a big department store in Dallas to order its shop-by-mail catalog. She called at 4:15 on a Monday afternoon. She talked for 9 minutes. How much did the call cost her?

7. Ramon heard that Los Angeles was called the "City of Angels." So at 2 o'clock one Tuesday afternoon, he called the Los Angeles City Hall and asked to speak with one.

He talked to an angry clerk for 5 minutes. How much did the call cost?

8. Kelly once called a peanut factory in Atlanta to order a couple pounds of peanuts. She called on a Thursday evening and talked for 4 minutes. How much did the call cost her?

9. Garry once called a rug factory in Sioux Falls to order some carpet for his apartment. He called on a Saturday morning and talked for 15 minutes. How much did his call cost?

10. One Tuesday morning at 10:00, Jana called a Boston bean company to ask about a good recipe for baking beans. She talked for 30 minutes. How much did the call cost her?

SKILL: Comparing unit prices of different sizes and brands of a product you want to buy.

Saving money has the Arithmians very excited about buying wisely. They are sure they can learn to save more when they go shopping, so Anja finds out exactly how to go about saving the most.

She discovers that products are packaged in different ways which makes a difference in the cost. These different ways of packaging are called units (pounds, pints, ounces, quarts, gallons, pieces, etc.).

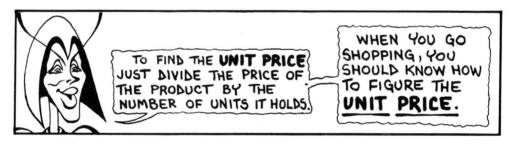

SAMPLE: Can holds 10 ounces. It costs $5.00. What is the price of each unit? (Unit? *ounces*)

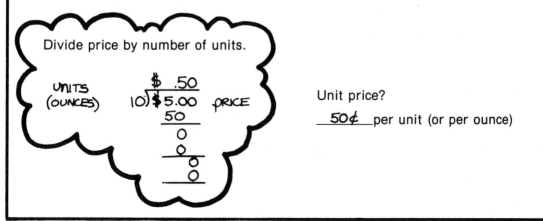

Divide price by number of units.

UNITS (OUNCES) $10)\overline{\$5.00}$ PRICE

Unit price?

___50¢___ per unit (or per ounce)

HERE'S ANOTHER SAMPLE THAT I'LL TRY.

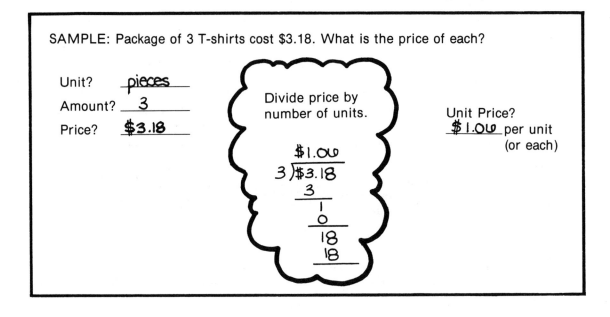

SAMPLE: Package of 3 T-shirts cost $3.18. What is the price of each?

Unit? __pieces__

Amount? __3__

Price? __$3.18__

Divide price by number of units.

$$\begin{array}{r} \$1.00 \\ 3\overline{\smash{)}\$3.18} \\ \underline{3} \\ 1 \\ 0 \\ 18 \\ \underline{18} \end{array}$$

Unit Price?

__$1.00__ per unit (or each)

For each of the following products, think of the *unit, amount* of units, *price.* Figure out the *unit price.* Round your answer to the nearest cent if necessary.

√ 1. Peaches, 16 ounces cost $1.15   Unit price? _____

2. Strawberries, 8 quarts cost $6.40   Unit price? _____

3. Gasoline, 23 gallons cost $34.27.   Unit price? _____

4. Nails, 5 pounds cost $3.75.   Unit price? _____

5. Plants, 9 plants for $25.83.   Unit price? _____

Buying Wisely

SAMPLE: (Figure the unit cost for each brand.)

This brand of mustard holds
8 ounces and costs 64¢.

Brand X

$$\begin{array}{r} 8¢ \\ 8\overline{)64¢} \\ \underline{64} \end{array}$$

UNIT PRICE: 8¢ PER UNIT (OUNCE)

This brand of mustard holds
6.5 ounces and costs 59¢.

Brand Z

$$\begin{array}{r} 9¢ \\ 6.5\overline{)59.0¢} \\ \underline{58\ 5} \\ 5 \end{array}$$

UNIT PRICE: 9¢ PER UNIT (OUNCE)

Which brand costs less?   BRAND X

You can do the same to compare different sizes of the same brand.

SAMPLE: (Figure the unit cost for each size.)

The "giant sized" box of Mother's Oatmeal holds 2 lbs. It costs $1.26.

$$
\begin{array}{r}
.63 \text{ per unit (lb.)} \\
2\,)\overline{\$1.26} \\
\underline{12} \\
6 \\
\underline{6}
\end{array}
$$

The "family sized" box of Mother's Oatmeal holds 1½ lbs. It costs $1.20.

$$
\begin{array}{r}
.80 \text{ per unit (lb.)} \\
1.5_\wedge\,)\overline{\$1.2_\wedge00} \\
\underline{120} \\
0 \\
\underline{0}
\end{array}
$$

Which size is cheaper? _the "giant size"_

GEE! THAT'S QUITE A SAVING!

If we can save that much, I'd better be sure I know how to compare prices correctly. Let me try a sample.

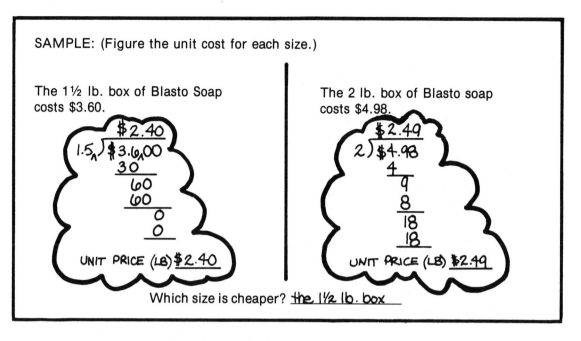

SAMPLE: (Figure the unit cost for each size.)

The 1½ lb. box of Blasto Soap costs $3.60.

$$\begin{array}{r} \$2.40 \\ 1.5_\wedge)\overline{\$3.6_\wedge 00} \\ \underline{30} \\ 60 \\ \underline{60} \\ 0 \\ \underline{0} \end{array}$$

UNIT PRICE (LB) $\underline{\$2.40}$

The 2 lb. box of Blasto soap costs $4.98.

$$\begin{array}{r} \$2.49 \\ 2)\overline{\$4.98} \\ \underline{4} \\ 9 \\ \underline{8} \\ 18 \\ \underline{18} \end{array}$$

UNIT PRICE (LB) $\underline{\$2.49}$

Which size is cheaper? <u>the 1½ lb. box</u>

YOU'VE GOT IT! BE SURE TO TRY THIS NEXT TIME YOU GO SHOPPING. IT WILL BE WORTH IT!

Figure the unit prices for each pair of products below. Round your answers to the nearest cent, then decide which item in each pair is least expensive per unit.

1. Cider: 1.6 gallons for $4.00 or 1.2 gallons for $3.75.

2. Soup: a 6 oz. can for $.18 or a 13 oz. can for $.24.

3. Ink: 4.1 pints for $1.84 or 3 pints for $1.75.

4. Instant potatoes: 17 oz. package for $1.29 or 8 oz. package for $.99.

5. Socks: 5 pairs for $9.98 or 3 pairs for $5.59.

6. Baseballs: 10 for $11.98 or 5 for $5.98.

7. Oranges: 1 lb. for $.79 or 2 lbs. for $1.50.

8. Candy bar: a 3.5 oz. bar for $.40 or a 2.5 oz. for $.20.

9. Coffee: a 5 lb. can for $9.98 or a 3 lb. can for $7.25.

10. Masking tape: a 25 ft. roll for $.62 or a 125 ft. roll for $1.32.

11. Diet cola: eight 10 oz. bottles for $1.55 or twelve 10 oz. bottles for $1.62.

12. Baked beans: a 15 oz. can for 90¢ or an 8 oz. can for 62¢.

For more practice in figuring the unit prices for pairs of products, solve the problems below. Round your answers to the nearest cent, then decide which item in each pair is least expensive per unit.

1. Green beans: a 24 oz. can for $1.28 or an 8 oz. can for $.27.

2. Milk: a 1 qt. carton for $.52 or a 1 gallon carton (4 qts.) for $1.89.

3. Bleach: a 16 oz. box for $.69 or a 6.5 oz. box for $.48.

4. Mayonnaise: a 48 oz. jar at $2.65 or a 12 oz. jar at $.98.

5. Wheat flour: a 10 lb. bag at $3.84 or a 5 lb. bag at $1.02.

6. House paint: a 2 gallon can at $7.15 or a 5 gallon can at $14.98.

7. Peanut butter: a 12 oz. jar at 89¢ or an 18 oz. jar at $1.27.

8. Spaghetti sauce: a 15.5 oz. jar at $.79 or a 32 oz. jar at $1.39.

9. Taco shells: package of 10 shells for $.61 or package of 20 for $1.07.

10. Frozen pizza: 13 oz. pizza at $1.45 or a 22 oz. pizza at $2.59.

SKILL: Figuring your total savings when you *buy in quantity.*

THERE IS ANOTHER WAY TO SAVE WHEN BUYING; SOMETIMES IT HELPS TO BUY **IN QUANTITY**.

IN OTHER WORDS, WHEN YOU BUY MORE, YOU MAY PAY A LOWER UNIT PRICE FOR EACH ITEM.

LOOK AT THIS SAMPLE TO SEE WHAT I MEAN.

SAMPLE:

Canned Green Beans
''Special''
41¢ each
or
3 for $1.19

Figure the total price for 3 cans bought separately.

$.41   PRICE PER CAN
x   3   CANS
$1.23   COST OF 3 CANS BOUGHT SEPARATELY

Subtract bargain price from cost if bought separately.

$1.23
−1.19   BARGAIN PRICE
$ .04

THAT LOOKS SIMPLE ENOUGH. LET ME DO ONE.

SAMPLE:

Records
$3.98 each
or
6 for $20.

If you buy 6 records now, you'll save $3.88

Figure the total price for 6 records bought separately.

$ 3.98
x   6
$23.88

Subtract the bargain price from cost bought separately.

$23.88
−20.00
$ 3.88

Figure the total savings for the following items if you buy in quantity. Round to the nearest cent when necessary.

√ 1. Rugs: $15.39 each or 3 for $39.00.

√ 2. Apples: $.65 per lb. or 2 lbs. for $1.29.

3. Bubble gum: 15¢ per pack or 10 packs for $1.39.

4. Anti-freeze: $1.50 per qt. or 4 qts. for $5.79.

5. Potatoes: a 10 lb. sack for $5.50 or two 10 lb. sacks for $10.00.

6. Corn: 26¢ per can or 4 cans for $1.00.

7. Mouse traps: $.38 each or 10 for $3.50.

8. Tape: 1 roll for $.69 or 10 rolls for $5.98.

9. Candles: $1.55 each or 2 for $3.00.

10. Ball point pens: $.49 each or 6 for $2.89.

11. Orange juice: 83¢ per qt. or 3 qts. for $2.39.

12. Pencils: 15¢ each or 10 for $1.00.

For additional practice in finding the total savings if you buy in quantity, solve the following problems. (Round to the nearest cent when necessary.)

1. Dish cloths: $.49 each or 3 for $1.29.

2. Sugar: $.98 a box or 2 boxes for $1.75.

3. Golf balls: $2.99 a package or 5 packages for $13.98.

4. Notebooks: $.69 each or 4 for $2.75.

5. Paper clips: $.89 per box or 10 boxes for $8.79.

6. Soap: $.49 per bar or 3 bars for $1.39.

7. Plants: $7.98 each or 2 for $14.99.

8. Chocolate bars: $.25 each or 8 for $1.98.

The Arithmians use three different kinds of transportation to get around town—the bus, a cab, or the subway. They are beginning to realize that they can save more money if they know how to figure the cost of each kind of transportation.

It is always a good idea to figure out about how much local transportation will be. Miro figured wrong one day, so he didn't have enough money to get back home.

TAKING A BUS

25¢ per ride

TAKING A SUBWAY

40¢ per ride

TAKING A CAB

80¢ for 1st half mile
40¢ each additional 1/4 mile

SAMPLE: One rainy day, Clyde took a cab from his apartment to the city bus barn; the distance was ½ mile. From the barn, he took a bus downtown; then he took the subway to work. How much did it cost him to get from home to work?

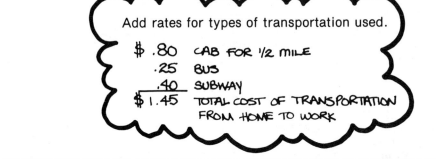

Add rates for types of transportation used.

$ .80 CAB FOR ½ MILE
  .25 BUS
  .40 SUBWAY
$1.45 TOTAL COST OF TRANSPORTATION FROM HOME TO WORK

SAMPLE: After Gene does his grocery shopping, he usually takes a cab home. The trip is 4¾ miles. How much does the transportation cost him?

Remember: Taxi costs 80¢ first ½ mile.
40¢ each additional ¼ mile.

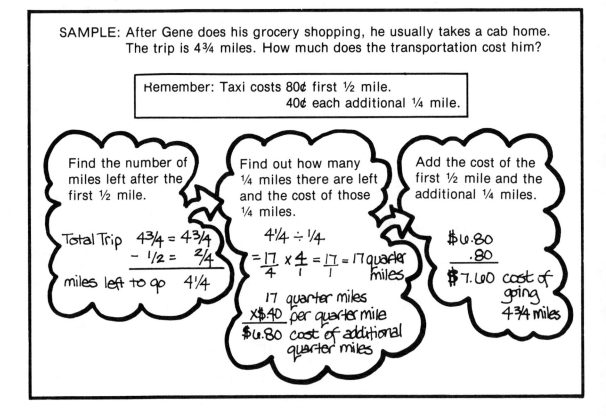

Find the number of miles left after the first ½ mile.

Total Trip   4¾ = 4¾
           − ½ = 2/4
miles left to go   4¼

Find out how many ¼ miles there are left and the cost of those ¼ miles.

$4¼ ÷ ¼$
$= \frac{17}{4} \times \frac{4}{1} = \frac{17}{1} = 17$ quarter miles

17 quarter miles
×$.40 per quarter mile
$6.80 cost of additional quarter miles

Add the cost of the first ½ mile and the additional ¼ miles.

$6.80
  .80
$7.60 cost of going 4¾ miles

Buying Wisely

Solve these problems. Use the same transportation costs the Arithmians used.

Cab - 80¢ first ½ mile 40¢ each additional ¼ mile	Bus - 25¢ per ride	Subway - 40¢ per ride

√ 1. Linda uses the bus 5 times a week and the subway 6 times a week. What is her total weekly cost for bus and subway rides?

√ 2. Glen uses the subway 40 times each month. The subway sells a special monthly pass for $12.50. The pass can be used for a subway ride as many times as the rider wants. How much would Glen save each month by buying a monthly pass?

3. Three days a week, Lewis takes the bus from his apartment to the city library. He uses the subway to get back home. How much does his trip to the library and back home again cost him each week?

4. Lisa and Brenda took a cab ride to see the River City dump. The trip out to the dump and back was a total of 23 miles. If they split the cost of the ride, how much did it cost each of them?

5. Tracey uses the city bus 30 times each month. The city sells a monthly bus pass costing $7.25. How much will she save by buying the monthly pass?

6. To get to the airport from Julie's apartment, you have to take a bus downtown, then a subway to the edge of the city. From there, the trip by cab is 3¼ miles. How much does it cost to go from Julie's apartment to the airport?

7. One day, Amy visited Vera. She took a bus downtown, then a subway to Vera's apartment. To get back home, she took the subway back downtown and took a bus home. What were Amy's total travel costs that day?

8. When Mike visits Hal at night, he always takes a cab. The ride to Hal's apartment is 3½ miles. How much does it cost Mike to take a cab to Hal's apartment?

For more practice, solve the following problems. Use the transportation costs given on page 157.

1. Roy once had to take a cab to the airport. The ride was 8¾ miles. How much did it cost him?

2. To get from the River City train station to the Sweltering Arms Hotel, you can take a bus downtown and then take a cab for the last three miles. What is the total cost of such a trip?

3. Pam once took a cab from downtown River City to a shopping mall in the suburbs. The trip was 6½ miles. How much did it cost?

4. When Geraldo goes to a movie, he takes the subway downtown and then takes a cab back home. The trip back home is 2¾ miles. What is the total travel cost for Geraldo, to go to and come back from the movies?

5. Judy takes the bus twice a day, Monday through Friday. The bus company offers a weekly pass for $2.00. The pass allows riders as many rides as they want. How much would Judy save each week by buying a weekly pass?

6. Warren and Marcie once split the cost of a cab ride to the River City Museum. The ride was a total of 4¾ miles. How much did it cost each of them for the ride?

Chapter 6
Self-Test

For items 1-3, figure the unit prices for each pair of products. Which is the *least* expensive per unit price? Round your answers to nearest cent. (See pages 147-152.)

1. A 2 lb. bag of apples for $.79
   A 5 lb. bag of apples for $1.69

2. A 64 oz. bottle of fruit juice for $1.28
   A 48 oz. bottle of fruit juice for $.98

3. A package of 4 scarves for $6.50
   A package of 7 scarves for $10.99

For items 4-6, figure the savings for buying in quantity. (See pages 153-154.)

4. Soup: 23¢ per can
                   - or -
                5 cans for $1.00

5. Grapefruit: 59¢ each
                   - or -
                6 for $3.00

6. Candy Bars: 25¢ each
                   - or -
                8 for $1.52

For items 7-9, solve each problem. (See pages 138-143.)

7. A dishwasher uses about 6 KWH per day. If each KWH is 8¢, how much will it cost to wash dishes for one week?

8. A toaster uses about 2 KWH every time it is used. If each KWH costs 9¢, what is the cost for using the toaster 42 times a week?

9. A refrigerator uses 5 KWH per day. At a rate of 8.5¢ per KWH, how much does it cost to run the refrigerator per day?

Use this rate chart to answer items 10-12. (See pages 143-147.)

From River City to:	Weekday Each		Evening Each		Night/Weekend Each	
	First Minute	Additional Minute	First Minute	Additional Minute	First Minute	Additional Minute
Atlanta	.50	.34	.32	.23	.20	.14
Boston	.52	.36	.33	.24	.20	.15
Chicago	.48	.34	.31	.23	.19	.14
Dallas	.50	.34	.32	.23	.20	.14
Denver	.50	.34	.32	.23	.20	.14
Los Angeles	.52	.36	.33	.24	.20	.15
Mpls.-St. Paul	.46	.32	.29	.21	.18	.13
New Orleans	.50	.34	.32	.23	.20	.14
New York	.52	.36	.33	.24	.20	.15
Omaha	.43	.28	.27	.19	.17	.12
San Francisco	.52	.36	.33	.24	.20	.15
Sioux Falls	.46	.32	.29	.21	.18	.13

Weekday:
8 AM - 5 PM,
Monday through Friday.

Evening:
5 PM - 11 PM,
Sunday through Friday.

Night/Weekend:
11 PM - 8 AM, any day;
All day Saturday:
8 AM - 5 PM, Sunday

10. Bonnie Stark called Sioux Falls on Thursday morning at 10 a.m. She talked for 7 minutes. What did the call cost?

11. On Saturday Jeff Corey called Los Angeles. His call lasted 21 minutes. How much did the call cost?

12. When he called Chicago, Juan talked for 30 minutes. He made the call Sunday evening at 9 o'clock. How much did this call cost?

Use this information to answer items 13-15. (See pages 155-158.)

Taking a cab:	Taking a bus:	Taking a subway:
80¢ for first ½ mile 40¢ each additional ¼ mile	25¢ per ride	40¢ per ride

13. Debbie takes the cab to work at the hospital, which is 3½ miles from her home. She takes the bus back home. What is her cost of traveling to and from work for a 5 day week?

14. Dave goes to the library three times a week to study. He takes a subway there and a bus back home. What does it cost each week for Dave to get to and from the library?

15. Oliver gets to his friend's house by taking a bus into town, then a subway to the other side of town. For the last 2½ miles, he takes a cab. What is the cost for him to travel to his friend's house?

Buying Wisely

USING THE BANK

USING BASIC MATH SKILLS TO SOLVE PROBLEMS RELATED TO BANKING.

KEY WORDS:

1. **Bank Statement:** a paper sent to you by your bank which tells how much money is in your account.

2. **Canceled Checks:** checks which have been cashed; so they cannot be cashed again. You can tell a check has been canceled by the markings the bank puts on the front and back of the check.

3. **Checkbook Register:** a booklet, kept with your checks, in which you keep a running balance of the checks you write and the deposits you make.

4. **Compounded Quarterly:** adding the interest you have earned on your savings account to your savings account balance every quarter of the year (every 3 months).

5. **Currency:** paper money; bills, not coins.

6. **Deposit Slip:** a form provided by your bank on which you write the exact amounts of money you are depositing into your checking or savings account.

7. **Interest:** the amount of money a bank pays you for keeping your money in the bank. The amount of interest depends upon the interest rate paid by the bank and the

balance in your account when the interest is figured.

8. **Interest Rate:** the percentage your bank pays you on the balance of your savings account.

9. **Reconciling a Checking Account:** making your checkbook register and bank statement show the same amount.

10. **Running Balance:** a balance which changes as you subtract amounts from it or add amounts to it.

11. **Service Charge:** an amount of money, usually small, your bank *may* charge you for keeping track of the money in your checking account.

SKILL: Figuring quarterly interest earned on a savings account balance.

Now that the Arithmians have been working for several months, they have been able to save some money. Miro reads in a newspaper ad that they can open a savings account at a bank. What puzzles him is that the ad states they can earn money by saving money at the bank. He tells this to Anja and Ranzo, so they all decide to go to the bank right away to find out more about it.

     Using the Bank

SAMPLE:

Balance x Interest Rate x Times (Quarter of a year)

$100   x   .06   x   ¼

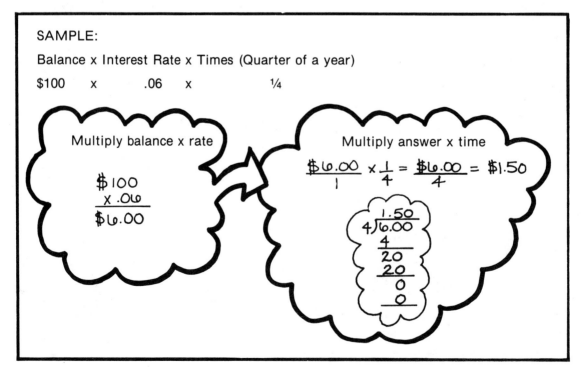

$100.00 Balance
  1.50 Quarterly Interest
———————
$101.50 New Balance

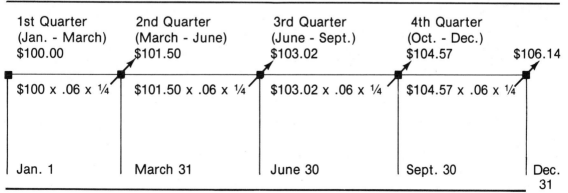

1st Quarter (Jan. - March) $100.00	2nd Quarter (March - June) $101.50	3rd Quarter (June - Sept.) $103.02	4th Quarter (Oct. - Dec.) $104.57	$106.14
$100 x .06 x ¼	$101.50 x .06 x ¼	$103.02 x .06 x ¼	$104.57 x .06 x ¼	
Jan. 1	March 31	June 30	Sept. 30	Dec. 31

Different kinds of banks pay different kinds of interest at different rates. Some pay interest every day, some every month. Always be sure you check your own bank to see what interest it pays. Whatever it is, the formula still holds true for figuring it. (Balance x Rate x Time.)

Try using the formula on these problems. Round your answers to the nearest cent when necessary.

√ 1. $560 x .05 x 1/4

2. $305.60 x .07 x 1/4

3. $1,085 x .045 x 1/4

√ 4. Hank saves money in a bank which pays a yearly interest rate of 4.5 percent. How much does he earn in a quarter on a balance of $750?

5. Carol's bank pays a yearly interest rate of 6%. How much will she earn in a quarter on a balance of $351.50?

6. First Federal Savings pays its savings account members a yearly interest rate of 4.9 percent. How much would a depositor earn in a quarter on a balance of $2,100?

7. At a yearly interest rate of 5.6 percent, how much would you earn in a quarter on $65?

8. Every quarter, Second National Bank pays interest at its yearly rate of 6%. How much would the quarterly interest on a balance of $506.50 be?

9. Alfred Asbury saves at a bank paying a yearly interest rate of 5.5%. How much interest will be earned in a quarter on a balance of $3,250?

10. At a yearly interest rate of 5%, how much would you earn in a quarter on a balance of $45?

11. Stan's bank pays a yearly interest of 6.5 percent. How much will Stan's interest be for a quarter on a balance of $950?

Here are some additional problems on figuring quarterly interest. Round your answers to the nearest cent when necessary.

1. Oscar Harris has a savings account that pays a yearly interest rate of 4.8%. How much does he earn in a quarter on a balance of $275.00?

2. Floyd Schwartz saves his money at a bank that pays a yearly interest rate of 6%. How much will he earn in a quarter on a balance of $565?

3. First National Bank pays its savings depositors a yearly interest rate of 5.5%. How much would a depositor earn in a quarter on a balance of $1,762?

4. How much would you earn in a quarter on $110 if the bank pays a yearly interest rate of 5.2%?

5. Every quarter the Chemical Corn Exchange Bank pays interest on its yearly rate of 6.7%. What would the quarterly interest be on a balance of $450?

6. Maynard Krim saves his money at a bank that pays a yearly interest rate of 7.9%. How much interest will be earned in this quarter on a balance of $37?

7. At a yearly interest rate of 6%, how much interest will be earned in a quarter on a balance of $2,605?

8. Steve Nestor's savings account pays a yearly interest rate of 4.5%. How much will Steve earn in interest in a quarter on a balance of $752?

9. At a bank paying 5.9% interest annually, how much will you earn in interest quarterly on a balance of $200?

10. Ricardo Moreno has a savings account at a bank paying 5.4% interest yearly. How much will Ricardo earn this quarter on $40?

SKILL: Filling out a bank deposit slip.

Since the Arithmians visited the bank, they realize there are many things they need to know about banking. Anja decides to go back to the bank the next day, and she learns all they'll need to know to do their banking.

DEPOSIT SLIP

CASH	CURRENCY	42	00
	COIN		68
List checks singly		17	42
		18	06
TOTAL		78	16
Less cash received			
NET DEPOSIT		78	16

1. In the slot for CURRENCY, write the value of *bills* deposited.

2. In the slot for COIN, write the value of *coins* deposited.

3. In the slots for CHECKS, list separately the value of each *check* deposited.

4. Add the values you have written. Write the sum in the TOTAL slot.

5. Write the total once again in the NET DEPOSIT slot. This is the amount of money that goes into your account.

1. List the checks separately and add to get their sum in TOTAL.
2. Write the amount of cash you want in the slot for LESS CASH RECEIVED.
3. Subtract this amount from TOTAL, writing the remainder in NET DEPOSIT.
   This is the amount that will go into your account.

DEPOSIT SLIP

CASH	CURRENCY		
	COIN		
List checks singly		$ 181	72
		19	38
TOTAL		201	10
Less cash received		72	19
NET DEPOSIT		128	91

Find the *Correct Total* and *Net Deposit* for each deposit slip below.

DEPOSIT SLIP

✓ 1.

CASH	CURRENCY	153	00
	COIN		94
List checks singly		18	63
		17	58
		13	40
TOTAL			
Less cash received			
NET DEPOSIT			

DEPOSIT SLIP

2.

CASH	CURRENCY		
	COIN		
List checks singly		153	49
		62	83
TOTAL			
Less cash received		73	84
NET DEPOSIT			

DEPOSIT SLIP

3.

CASH	CURRENCY		
	COIN		
List checks singly		5	08
		164	19
TOTAL			
Less cash received		83	50
NET DEPOSIT			

DEPOSIT SLIP

4.

CASH	CURRENCY	419	00
	COIN	1	34
List checks singly		25	00
		16	98
		102	41
TOTAL			
Less cash received			
NET DEPOSIT			

DEPOSIT SLIP

5.

CASH	CURRENCY	63	00
	COIN	3	45
List checks singly		28	64
		19	99
TOTAL			
Less cash received			
NET DEPOSIT			

DEPOSIT SLIP

6.

CASH	CURRENCY		
	COIN		
List checks singly		43	00
		18	75
		32	94
		17	68
TOTAL			
Less cash received		66	48
NET DEPOSIT			

DEPOSIT SLIP

7.

CASH	CURRENCY	48	00
	COIN		16
List checks singly		9	59
		17	68
		5	47
		163	09
TOTAL			
Less cash received			
NET DEPOSIT			

DEPOSIT SLIP

8.

CASH	CURRENCY		
	COIN		
List checks singly		18	50
		7	28
		13	56
TOTAL			
Less cash received			
NET DEPOSIT			

DEPOSIT SLIP

9.

CASH	CURRENCY	18	00
	COIN		
List checks singly		16	91
		82	05
		17	83
TOTAL			
Less cash received			
NET DEPOSIT			

DEPOSIT SLIP

10.

CASH	CURRENCY		
	COIN		
List checks singly		46	82
		17	09
		463	82
TOTAL			
Less cash received		210	68
NET DEPOSIT			

DEPOSIT SLIP

11.

CASH	CURRENCY	105	00
	COIN		94
List checks singly		28	16
		351	78
TOTAL			
Less cash received			
NET DEPOSIT			

DEPOSIT SLIP

12.

CASH	CURRENCY		
	COIN		94
List checks singly		47	30
		200	00
		5	17
		356	92
TOTAL			
Less cash received			
NET DEPOSIT			

For additional practice in filling out deposit slips, complete the following sample slips.

DEPOSIT SLIP

1.

CASH	CURRENCY	210	00
	COIN		85
List checks singly		35	00
		21	76
TOTAL			
Less cash received		28	34
NET DEPOSIT			

DEPOSIT SLIP

2.

CASH	CURRENCY	28	00
	COIN	3	78
List checks singly		103	66
		44	50
TOTAL			
Less cash received			
NET DEPOSIT			

DEPOSIT SLIP

3.

CASH	CURRENCY	42	00
	COIN		
List checks singly		466	25
		321	63
		101	02
		6	27
TOTAL			
Less cash received			
NET DEPOSIT			

DEPOSIT SLIP

4.

CASH	CURRENCY		
	COIN		
List checks singly		98	20
		60	54
		7	26
TOTAL			
Less cash received		25	00
NET DEPOSIT			

DEPOSIT SLIP

5.

CASH	CURRENCY	67	00
	COIN	26	02
List checks singly		125	67
		326	44
		91	08
TOTAL			
Less cash received			
NET DEPOSIT			

DEPOSIT SLIP

6.

CASH	CURRENCY		
	COIN	3	71
List checks singly		23	55
		6	21
TOTAL			
Less cash received			
NET DEPOSIT			

DEPOSIT SLIP

7.

CASH	CURRENCY		
	COIN		
List checks singly		41	27
		103	44
		219	18
TOTAL			
Less cash received		175	77
NET DEPOSIT			

DEPOSIT SLIP

8.

CASH	CURRENCY	500	00
	COIN		
List checks singly		6	26
		7	99
		19	76
TOTAL			
Less cash received			
NET DEPOSIT			

DEPOSIT SLIP

9.

CASH	CURRENCY		
	COIN		73
List checks singly		36	46
		29	05
		5	07
TOTAL			
Less cash received			
NET DEPOSIT			

DEPOSIT SLIP

10.

CASH	CURRENCY	242	00
	COIN	3	19
List checks singly		52	00
		4	41
TOTAL			
Less cash received			
NET DEPOSIT			

Using the Bank

DEPOSIT SLIP

11.

CASH	CURRENCY	1	00
	COIN		45
List checks singly		3	98
		2	77
		105	22
TOTAL			
Less cash received			
NET DEPOSIT			

DEPOSIT SLIP

12.

CASH	CURRENCY		
	COIN		
List checks singly		80	90
		44	04
		19	80
		2	02
TOTAL			
Less cash received		50	47
NET DEPOSIT			

DEPOSIT SLIP

13.

CASH	CURRENCY	180	00
	COIN		
List checks singly		75	94
		366	21
		200	35
		91	47
TOTAL			
Less cash received			
NET DEPOSIT			

DEPOSIT SLIP

14.

CASH	CURRENCY		
	COIN	9	95
List checks singly		41	12
		291	50
		137	79
TOTAL			
Less cash received			
NET DEPOSIT			

DEPOSIT SLIP

15.

CASH	CURRENCY	200	00
	COIN		81
List checks singly		78	94
		151	67
TOTAL			
Less cash received			
NET DEPOSIT			

DEPOSIT SLIP

16.

CASH	CURRENCY	18	00
	COIN	7	71
List checks singly		40	31
		27	17
		135	04
TOTAL			
Less cash received			
NET DEPOSIT			

DEPOSIT SLIP

17.

CASH	CURRENCY		
	COIN		
List checks singly		94	12
		70	00
		5	31
TOTAL			
Less cash received		112	08
NET DEPOSIT			

DEPOSIT SLIP

18.

CASH	CURRENCY	404	00
	COIN		
List checks singly		96	10
		244	91
		108	20
TOTAL			
Less cash received			
NET DEPOSIT			

SKILL: Writing checks properly.

176   Using the Bank

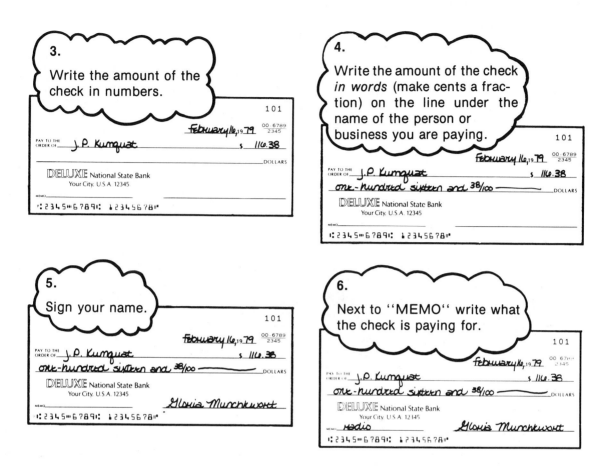

3. Write the amount of the check in numbers.

4. Write the amount of the check *in words* (make cents a fraction) on the line under the name of the person or business you are paying.

5. Sign your name.

6. Next to "MEMO" write what the check is paying for.

See if you or your teacher can get some blank checks from your local bank. Practice writing out a check to pay for each of the following bills.

√ 1.

SLOPPY JOE'S GRILLE

One extra special, extraordinary, super deluxe hamburger.

TOTAL: $15.83

√ 2.

PRACTICAL APPLIANCE COMPANY

One combination electric toothbrush and shoe polisher.

TOTAL: $35.50

3.

OLD HAT CLOTHIERS, INC.

Lifetime supply of thermal socks and underwear.

TOTAL: $238.41

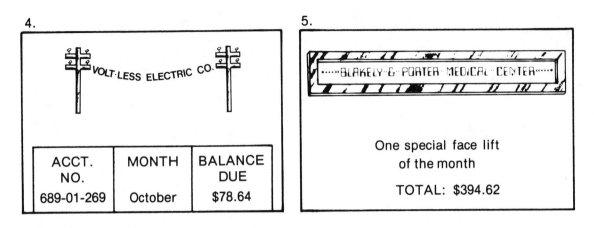

4.

VOLT-LESS ELECTRIC CO.

ACCT. NO.	MONTH	BALANCE DUE
689-01-269	October	$78.64

5.

······BLAKELY & PORTER MEDICAL CENTER······

One special face lift
of the month

TOTAL: $394.62

6.

HAPPY JOHN'S groceries

One week's supply
of cat food.

TOTAL: $56.40

7.

MONKEY WRENCH REPAIR SERVICE

Tune-up and required
parts replacement

TOTAL: $483.17

8.

HOT WATER POWER CO.

ACCT. NO.

2AX-14682-0

Service for August

TOTAL: $18.56

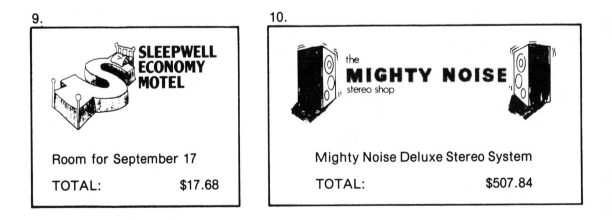

9.

SLEEPWELL ECONOMY MOTEL

Room for September 17

TOTAL: $17.68

10.

the MIGHTY NOISE stereo shop

Mighty Noise Deluxe Stereo System

TOTAL: $507.84

Now that they know how to write checks properly, Ranzo and Miro wonder what happens to the check when they pay someone with it instead of cash.

THE PERSON YOU WRITE THE CHECK TO TAKES IT TO HER BANK FOR MONEY. THEN THAT BANK SENDS IT TO YOUR BANK,...

...SO IT CAN BE PAID OFF WITH MONEY IN **YOUR** ACCOUNT. NOW 2 THINGS CAN HAPPEN:

GOOD	BAD
If your account has enough money to cover the amount of the check . . .	If your account does *NOT* have enough money to cover the amount of the check . . .
a) . . . your bank deducts the amount of the check from your account . . .	a) . . .the check "bounces" from your bank back to the person you gave it to . . .
b) . . . and sends the money over to the first bank.	b) . . . and that person can take you you to court to collect the money you owe.
c) Your bank stamps the check "canceled" to show the check has been cashed for money.	·c) Your bank will charge you a fee if your checks "bounce."

SKILL: Keeping a running balance in a checkbook register.

The Arithmians now realize why they should always have enough money in their checking accounts. They certainly do not want any checks to "bounce." The only way to be sure this does not happen is by keeping the accounts *balanced.* Anja explains to Miro and Ranzo that every checkbook comes with a *checkbook register* or *balance book.* In the register or balance book, all information about checks written and money deposited should be recorded.

A *running balance* of the money left in the accounts should be kept, too. Anja explains that the running balance is a way of saying that the balance *changes* every time the account is used.

CHECK NO	DATE	CHECKS ISSUED TO OR DESCRIPTION OF DEPOSIT	AMOUNT OF CHECK		√ T	AMOUNT OF DEPOSIT	BALANCE 277	28
175	5/23	Hamptman Jewelers	44	72			44	72
		bracelet					232	56
Deposit	5/25	cash				100 00	100	00
							332	56
176	5/27	Dr. Linton	20	00			20	00
		check-up					312	56
177	5/27	Water Dept.	12	66			12	66
		water bill					299	90
178	5/28	The News Times	5	04			5	04
		newspaper ad					294	86
Deposit	5/31	paycheck				349 50	349	50
							644	36
179	6/1	Hillside Apartments	250 00				250	00
		rent					394	36

Using the Bank

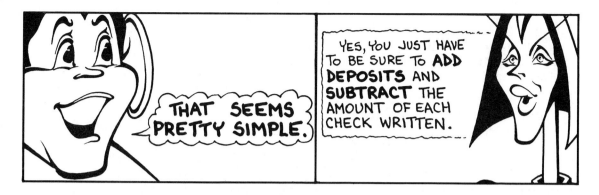

Use the following checks and deposits to find how to complete the checkbook register below. This will give a *running balance* of the money left in the account. Start with a balance of $225.64. The first check and deposit are already entered. (Do your work on a separate sheet of paper.)

CHECK NO	DATE	CHECKS ISSUED TO OR DESCRIPTION OF DEPOSIT	(-) AMOUNT OF CHECK		✓ T	(+) AMOUNT OF DEPOSIT		BALANCE	
								225	64
253	2-8	fred's Bookstore	19	63				19	63
		(books)						206	01
Deposit	2-9					5	17	5	17
		(birthday present)						211	18
254	2-11								
255	2-16								
Deposit	2-19	cash							
256	2-21								
257	2-21								
Deposit	2-23	cash							
Deposit	2-25	check							
258	2-28								
Deposit	2-28	paycheck							

Checks written:

1. Check No. 253, written Feb. 8 to Fred's Bookstore, for a dictionary. Amount: $19.63.

2. Check No. 254, written Feb. 11, to Rose's Gift Shoppe, for a birthday present. Amount: $5.17.

3. Check No. 255, written Feb. 16 to Mona's Flowers, for a house plant. Amount: $19.86.

4. Check No. 256, written Feb. 21 to Bill's Bootery, for some new shoes. Amount: $32.50.

5. Check No. 257, written Feb. 21 to Carla's Crockery, for a bowl. Amount: $5.25.

6. Check No. 258, written Feb. 26 to Zigg's Wigs, for a wig. Amount: $38.62.

Deposits made:

1. On Feb. 9, a $5.17 check from a friend for your birthday.

2. On Feb. 19, $36.85 in cash.

3. On Feb. 23, $13.44 in cash.

4. On Feb. 25, a $76.18 check from a friend, repaying a loan.

5. On Feb. 28, $515.75; paycheck.

Anja explains to the other Arithmians that they must be very careful when figuring a running balance because it is very easy to make mistakes. After figuring a running balance, it should always be checked; there is always a chance you'll find an error.

In each register shown below, there is an error of addition or subtraction in the running balance. Copy each running balance on a separate sheet, and then check each until you discover the error. Correct the error and the following entries in the running balance.

✓ 1.

CHECK NO	DATE	CHECKS ISSUED TO OR DESCRIPTION OF DEPOSIT	AMOUNT OF CHECK		✓ T	AMOUNT OF DEPOSIT	BALANCE	
							341	06
101	4-1	Chip's Chops	5	14			5	14
		(pork chops)					335	92
102	4-3	Hallelujah Bible Co.	18	04			18	04
		(Bibles)					317	88
Deposit	4-5	IRS return				198 98	198	98
							416	76
103	4-9	Dr. P. J. Worrywort	37	58			37	58
		(office visit)					379	18
Deposit	4-12	paycheck				763 90	763	90
							1,143	08
104	4-19	Horsepower Utility Co.	86	47			86	47
		(gas & electric bill)					1,056	61

2.

CHECK NO	DATE	CHECKS ISSUED TO OR DESCRIPTION OF DEPOSIT	AMOUNT OF CHECK (–)		✓ T	AMOUNT OF DEPOSIT (+)		BALANCE	
								58	17
deposit	3-1	paycheck				597	18	597	18
								655	35
54	3-3	George Pay up rent	142	91				142	91
								512	44
55	3-4	Silver Platter Cafe (dinner for 4)	38	90				38	90
								463	54
deposit	3-7	J.L. loan payment				57	82	57	82
								521	36
56	3-16	Gold-Plated Toothpick Co. (1 gold-plated toothpick)	5	68				5	68
								515	68
57	3-18	Doubleknitsville (slacks)	11	29				11	29
								504	39

3.

CHECK NO	DATE	CHECKS ISSUED TO OR DESCRIPTION OF DEPOSIT	AMOUNT OF CHECK (–)		✓ T	AMOUNT OF DEPOSIT (+)		BALANCE	
								100	96
18	8-10	Pleasant Listening Records Co. (records)	25	13				25	13
								126	09
19	8-12	Max's Bar and Grill (meal)	10	06				10	06
								116	03
20	8-18	Clem's Kodiddlehoppers (1 Kodiddlehoppers)	39	99				39	99
								76	04
Deposit	8-25	paycheck				458	62	458	62
								534	66
21	8-26	Pa Bull Phone Co. (phone bill)	137	16				137	16
								397	50
Deposit	8-31	refund for check no.001				17	63	17	63
								379	87

4.

CHECK NO.	DATE	CHECKS ISSUED TO OR DESCRIPTION OF DEPOSIT	AMOUNT OF CHECK (−)	✓ T	AMOUNT OF DEPOSIT (+)	BALANCE	
						1,652	87
4	1-5	Abracadabra Magic Shop	116 58			116	58
		(magicians tuxedo)				1,535	29
deposit	1-10	paycheck			593 27	593	27
						942	02
5	1-12	Abracadabra Magic Shop	36 19			36	19
		(rabbit)				905	83
deposit	1-15	performance fee			15 23	15	23
						890	60
6	1-16	Abracadabra Magic Shop	28 87			28	87
		(straight jacket)				861	73
deposit	1-27	performance fee			27 16	27	16
						834	57

5.

CHECK NO.	DATE	CHECKS ISSUED TO OR DESCRIPTION OF DEPOSIT	AMOUNT OF CHECK (−)	✓ T	AMOUNT OF DEPOSIT (+)	BALANCE	
						362	15
305	11-8	Bill's Auto Supply	103 59			103	59
		(fog horn)				158	56
306	11-12	County Court House	18 26			18	26
		(fine for blowing fog horn)				140	30
deposit	11-13	paycheck			452 65	452	65
						592	95
307	11-21	Bill's Auto Supply	5 25			5	25
		(muffler for fog horn)				587	70
308	11-25	County Court House	22 98			22	98
		(fine for blowing fog horn)				564	72
309	11-28	Dr. E. R. Blake	17 36			17	36
		(office visit)				546	36

Using the Bank

For more practice in finding errors in the running balance of a check register, check the addition and subtraction in each of the check registers shown below. Copy each on a separate sheet of paper, and correct the running balances as you discover the errors.

1.

CHECK NO	DATE	CHECKS ISSUED TO OR DESCRIPTION OF DEPOSIT	(-) AMOUNT OF CHECK	√T	(+) AMOUNT OF DEPOSIT	BALANCE	
						557	96
201	3-6	Hawk's Grocery	25 75			25	75
		(party supplies)				532	21
202	3-8	Costume Shop	15 88			15	88
		(costume rental)				548	09
203	3-9	Anderson's Drugs	2 57			2	57
		(aspirin, antacid)				545	52
Deposit	3-9	prize			50 00	50	00
						595	52
204	3-12	Jack's Towing	10 30			10	30
						585	22
205	3-13	McDuck Insurance	250 00			250	00
						235	22

2.

CHECK NO	DATE	CHECKS ISSUED TO OR DESCRIPTION OF DEPOSIT	(-) AMOUNT OF CHECK	√T	(+) AMOUNT OF DEPOSIT	BALANCE	
						37	52
009	6-1	Master Music Shop	18 77			18	77
		(guitar strings)				18	75
deposit	6-2	paycheck			150 00	150	00
						168	75
010	6-4	Master Music Shop	6 52			6	52
		(music)				168	75
011	6-6	Inkmore Printers	19 44			19	44
		(business cards)				149	31
deposit	6-6	paycheck			150 00	150	00
						299	31
012	6-12	Musicians' Union	212 64			212	64
		(dues)				86	67

3.

CHECK NO	DATE	CHECKS ISSUED TO OR DESCRIPTION OF DEPOSIT	AMOUNT OF CHECK		✓T	AMOUNT OF DEPOSIT		BALANCE	
								100	15
101	2-4	Bobby Jones	5	50				5	50
		(shoveled snow)						100	65
102	2-6	Rounder Tire Co.	88	19				88	19
		(snow tires)						11	66
103	2-7	Bill's Service	10	30				10	30
		(start car)						1	36
deposit	2-7	from savings				50	00	50	00
								51	36
104	2-9	Stu's Boots	26	51				26	51
		(boots)						24	85
deposit	2-10	baby sitting fee				17	50	17	50
								42	35

4.

CHECK NO	DATE	CHECKS ISSUED TO OR DESCRIPTION OF DEPOSIT	AMOUNT OF CHECK		✓T	AMOUNT OF DEPOSIT		BALANCE	
								462	01
293	9-6	Dolly Preschool	50	66				50	66
		tuition						416	35
deposit	9-6	paycheck				397	55	397	55
								803	90
294	9-10	Bo-bo's Clothing	29	40				29	40
		(dress)						774	50
deposit	9-12	paycheck				608	14	608	14
								1382	64
295	9-13	Bank	500	00				500	00
		(savings deposit)						882	64
296	9-13	Bank	252	12				252	12
		(house payment)						630	52

SKILL: Reconciling your checking account.

The Arithmians have just received a checking account *statement* along with their canceled checks in the mail. Miro and Ranzo can't understand why the checks they wrote some time ago have been returned. Anja reminds them that these checks have already been cashed and marked "canceled" by the bank; these markings are on the front and back of the check.

Even though the checks can't be used again, the bank returned them to the Arithmians to help them check their running balance. The canceled checks are also excellent receipts; you should keep them filed as proof of payment.

Anja explains that the bank *sometimes* sends deposit slips along with the statement and canceled checks. These can all be used to help check your running balance. The *statement* shows a running balance of money that you put in and take out of your account.

DELUXE National State Bank
Your City, U.S.A. 12345

YOUR NAME
YOUR ADDRESS

ACCOUNT NUMBER		STATEMENT DATE	

CHECKS SUBTRACTED FROM ACCOUNT	DEPOSITS ADDED TO ACCOUNT	DATE	BALANCE
		8/30	$600.00
$100.00		9/2	500.00
	$250.00	9/6	750.00
349.50		9/10	400.50
.80 SC		9/30	399.70
TOTAL CHECKS & SERVICE CHARGE	TOTAL DEPOSITS		BALANCE THIS STATEMENT
$450.30	$250.00		$399.70

Under the heading "Checks Subtracted From Account," it lists the checks which you have written. This shows the bank has received them, and that they have been deducted, or subtracted, from your account.

Anja further explains the statement by telling Ranzo and Miro to look under the heading "Deposits Added To Your Account." Here the bank lists the amount of money that was deposited last month. She tells them that the "Balance" shows the amount of money they had in the bank on the date of the statement.

1. Don't forget to deduct *service charge* (if your bank has this fee) in your register. Write "service charge" where you usually write a check number. Subtract it to get a new balance.

2. Sometimes you will list a check on your register that is not on your statement, because the statement lists only the checks that have been cashed and canceled. If this happens, your check has probably not been cashed yet.

3. Make sure all your deposits have had time to be recorded by the bank. If the deposit is *not* included, perhaps the statement was mailed to you before you made the deposit.

Using the Bank

Step 1: Make sure you subtract in your checkbook register any service charge that may be deducted from your account.

CHECK NO	DATE	CHECKS ISSUED TO OR DESCRIPTION OF DEPOSIT	AMOUNT OF CHECK	✓T	AMOUNT OF DEPOSIT	BALANCE	
						600	00
351	9-2	Random's Service	100	00		100	00
		(car repair)				500	00
deposit	9-6	Paycheck			250 00	250	00
						750	00
352	9-10	Bank Charge Card	349	50		349	50
		(monthly payment)				400	50
Service							80
Charge						399	70

Step 2: In your checkbook register, put a check mark (✓) in the proper column for all the canceled checks and deposit slips sent to you by the bank.

CHECK NO	DATE	CHECKS ISSUED TO OR DESCRIPTION OF DEPOSIT	AMOUNT OF CHECK	✓T	AMOUNT OF DEPOSIT	BALANCE	
						600	00
398	6-1	Zelda's Zig Zag Sewing	100	00	✓	100	00
		Shop (sewing machine)				500	00
399	6-3	Forest View Apartments	349	50	✓	349	50
		(rent)				150	50
deposit	6-13	Overtime pay			✓	250 00	250	00
						400	50
400	6-29	Caine's Mail Order	50	00		50	00
		(cookware)				350	50
deposit	7-1	Paycheck			550 00	550	00
						900	50

Step 3: Look on the back of your statement. On the back of the statement, you will find a form for the balances of your checkbook register and the bank statement. *Remember:* To reconcile the balances means to make them show the same amount. Beside ''Balance Shown on This Statement'', write in the balance recorded on your bank statement.

```
+------------------------------------------------------------------------+
|                                                                        |
|    CHECKS NOT LISTED ON             BALANCE SHOWN                       |
|      THIS STATEMENT                 ON THIS STATEMENT    $_____ |
|                                                                        |
|  +----------+--------+------+    ADD +                                  |
|  | NO.      | $      |      |                                          |
|  |----------|--------|------|       DEPOSITS NOT SHOWN                  |
|  |          |        |      |       ON THIS STATEMENT                   |
|  |----------|--------|------|                (IF ANY)  $_____   |
|  |          |        |      |                          _____   |
|  |----------|--------|------|                          _____   |
|  |          |        |      |                                          |
|  |----------|--------|------|    SUBTOTAL              $_____   |
|  |          |        |      |    SUBTRACT-                              |
|  |----------|--------|------|                                          |
|  |          |        |      | --> CHECKS NOT LISTED    $_____   |
|  |----------|--------|------|                                          |
|  |          |        |      |                                          |
|  |----------|--------|------|    RECONCILED BALANCE    $_____   |
|  |          |        |      |                                          |
|  |----------|--------|------|    SHOULD AGREE WITH CHECK BOOK          |
|  |  TOTAL   |        |      |    BALANCE AFTER SUBTRACTING SERVICE     |
|  +----------+--------+------+    CHARGE FROM CHECK BOOK BALANCE.       |
|                                                                        |
+------------------------------------------------------------------------+
```

Step 4: In the space marked ''Deposits Not Shown on This Statement'' write the amounts of the deposits you've made that are *not* recorded on your bank statement. You do this by finding the deposit in your checkbook register that you did not check (✓). Write the amount of this unchecked deposit on the line provided.

Step 5: Add the amounts of ''Statement Balance'' and ''Deposits'' together. Write the sum in the slot beside ''Subtotal.''

Step 6: Write the numbers and amounts of any checks you've written that are *not* listed on bank's statement. You can find these by finding the checks in your checkbook register that you have *not* given a check mark. Write the number and amount in the space provided under ''Checks Not Listed on This Statement.''

Step 7: Add the amount of ''Total Checks Not Listed'' and write that amount in the line provided next to ''Checks Not Listed.''

Step 8: Subtract the amount of the ''Checks Not Listed'' from ''Subtotal.'' Write the difference next to the ''Reconciled Balance''. This amount should be exactly the amount of the last balance of your checkbook register.

Using the Bank

Anja tells Ranzo that if the balance of the checkbook register and bank statement do not reconcile the first time, he should recheck his calculations in his checkbook register and reconcilement form. She also tells Ranzo to make sure all the numbers are recorded correctly. Anja reminds Ranzo *not* to forget any service charge from the checkbook register.

Here are six problems in reconciling or balancing a bank statement. For each problem, find the *Subtotal, Total Checks Not Listed,* and *Reconciled Balance.* Sample reconcilement forms are provided, but do your work on a separate sheet of paper.

✓ 1.

CHECKS NOT LISTED ON THIS STATEMENT		
NO.	$	
605	38	67
606	94	08
607	138	92
TOTAL		

BALANCE SHOWN
ON THIS STATEMENT $ **758.63**

ADD +

DEPOSITS NOT SHOWN
ON THIS STATEMENT
(IF ANY) $ **52.75**

_____

_____

SUBTOTAL $_____

SUBTRACT-

CHECKS NOT LISTED $_____

RECONCILED BALANCE $_____

SHOULD AGREE WITH CHECK BOOK
BALANCE AFTER SUBTRACTING SERVICE
CHARGE FROM CHECK BOOK BALANCE.

✓ 2.

CHECKS NOT LISTED ON THIS STATEMENT		
NO.	$	
101	159	62
102	8	75
103	52	86
TOTAL		

BALANCE SHOWN
ON THIS STATEMENT $ **17.57**

ADD +

DEPOSITS NOT SHOWN
ON THIS STATEMENT
(IF ANY) $ **602.50**
37.94

_____

SUBTOTAL $_____

SUBTRACT-

CHECKS NOT LISTED $_____

RECONCILED BALANCE $_____

SHOULD AGREE WITH CHECK BOOK
BALANCE AFTER SUBTRACTING SERVICE
CHARGE FROM CHECK BOOK BALANCE.

3.

CHECKS NOT LISTED ON THIS STATEMENT			BALANCE SHOWN ON THIS STATEMENT $ **1,652.90**
NO.	$		ADD +
794	186	52	
795	395	89	DEPOSITS NOT SHOWN
796	6	47	ON THIS STATEMENT
797	9	68	(IF ANY) $
798	21	53	
799	41	26	
800	11	99	SUBTOTAL $
801	5	42	SUBTRACT-
			CHECKS NOT LISTED $
			RECONCILED BALANCE $
			SHOULD AGREE WITH CHECK BOOK
			BALANCE AFTER SUBTRACTING SERVICE
TOTAL			CHARGE FROM CHECK BOOK BALANCE.

4.

CHECKS NOT LISTED ON THIS STATEMENT			BALANCE SHOWN ON THIS STATEMENT $ **58.45**
NO.	$		ADD +
562	162	18	
563	75	00	DEPOSITS NOT SHOWN
564	3	14	ON THIS STATEMENT
565	7	95	(IF ANY) $ **593.60**
			17.82
			23.94
			SUBTOTAL $
			SUBTRACT-
			CHECKS NOT LISTED $
			RECONCILED BALANCE $
			SHOULD AGREE WITH CHECK BOOK
			BALANCE AFTER SUBTRACTING SERVICE
TOTAL			CHARGE FROM CHECK BOOK BALANCE.

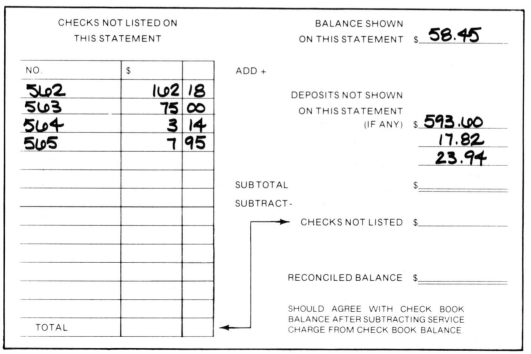

5.

CHECKS NOT LISTED ON THIS STATEMENT			
NO.	$		
NONE			
TOTAL			

BALANCE SHOWN
ON THIS STATEMENT $ **362.01**

ADD +

DEPOSITS NOT SHOWN
ON THIS STATEMENT
(IF ANY) $ **15.98**
163.05
10.15

SUBTOTAL $_____

SUBTRACT-

→ CHECKS NOT LISTED $_____

RECONCILED BALANCE $_____

SHOULD AGREE WITH CHECK BOOK
BALANCE AFTER SUBTRACTING SERVICE
CHARGE FROM CHECK BOOK BALANCE.

←

6.

CHECKS NOT LISTED ON THIS STATEMENT		
NO.	$	
670	150	00
671	15	87
672	48	63
673	19	19
674	8	67
675	13	41
676	21	48
677	10	91
TOTAL		

BALANCE SHOWN
ON THIS STATEMENT $ **18.4**

ADD +

DEPOSITS NOT SHOWN
ON THIS STATEMENT
(IF ANY) $ **573.64**
15.89

SUBTOTAL $_____

SUBTRACT-

→ CHECKS NOT LISTED $_____

RECONCILED BALANCE $_____

SHOULD AGREE WITH CHECK BOOK
BALANCE AFTER SUBTRACTING SERVICE
CHARGE FROM CHECK BOOK BALANCE.

←

Chapter 7
Self-Test

Use the bank deposit slip shown below to answer 1 and 2. (See pages 169-176.)

DEPOSIT SLIP

CASH	CURRENCY	42	00
	COIN	4	62
List checks singly		18	41
		238	64
		81	25
TOTAL			
Less cash received			
NET DEPOSIT			

1. What amount of money should be in the TOTAL space?

2. What amount of money should be in the NET DEPOSIT space?

Use this bank deposit slip to answer 3 and 4. (See pages 169-176.)

DEPOSIT SLIP

CASH	CURRENCY		
	COIN		
List checks singly		38	46
		123	72
		36	00
		16	25
TOTAL			
Less cash received		47	23
NET DEPOSIT			

3. What amount of money should be in the TOTAL space?

4. What amount of money should be in the NET DEPOSIT space?

Solve each problem. Round your answer to the nearest cent if necessary. (See pages 162-169.)

5. A bank pays 6% yearly interest on savings accounts. What is the amount of interest earned in a quarter on a balance of $400?

6. Peter's bank pays 5.5% yearly interest. How much will he earn in a quarter on a balance of $800.00?

7. A bank pays 6.2 percent interest on savings accounts. What is the amount of interest earned in a quarter on a balance of $730?

Use the checks shown below to complete items 8-10. (See pages 176-179.)

JAMES C. MORRISON
1765 SHERIDAN DRIVE
YOUR CITY, U.S.A.   12345

102

August 16 19 80   00-6789 / 2345

PAY TO THE ORDER OF   Dr. Lois Pinehill $ 75.00

Seventy-five and no/100 ———————— DOLLARS

DELUXE National State Bank
Your City, U.S.A. 12345

MEMO   Eye Exam

⑆:2345⑈6789⑆: 12345678⑆

JAMES C. MORRISON
1765 SHERIDAN DRIVE
YOUR CITY, U.S.A.   12345

103

August 17 19 80   00-6789 / 2345

PAY TO THE ORDER OF   Mitchell's Cozy Pantry $ 33.58

Thirty-three and 58/100 ———————— DOLLARS

DELUXE National State Bank
Your City, U.S.A. 12345

MEMO   Groceries   James C. Morrison

⑆:2345⑈6789⑆: 12345678⑆

Check 104

JAMES C. MORRISON
1765 SHERIDAN DRIVE
YOUR CITY, U.S.A.   12345

104

August 21 19 80   00-6789 / 2345

PAY TO THE ORDER OF Sam's Shoe Palace $ 3.92

3 and 92 ————————————————————— DOLLARS

DELUXE National State Bank
Your City, U.S.A. 12345

MEMO Shoe repair   James C. Morrison

⑈ ⑆2345⑈6789⑈ 12345678⑈

Check 105

JAMES C. MORRISON
1765 SHERIDAN DRIVE
YOUR CITY, U.S.A.   12345

105

August 30 19 80   00-6789 / 2345

PAY TO THE ORDER OF Hank's Hardware Hotel $ 79.00/99

Seventy-nine and 99/100 ———————————— DOLLARS

DELUXE National State Bank
Your City, U.S.A. 12345

MEMO tools   James C. Morrison

⑈ ⑆2345⑈6789⑈ 12345678⑈

8. What is the number of the check whose amount in numerals is written incorrectly?

9. What is the number of the check whose amount in words is written incorrectly?

10. What is the number of the check which is made up completely and correctly?

Find the correct balance for the last box in each checkbook register shown below. (See pages 179-186.)

11.

CHECK NO	DATE	CHECKS ISSUED TO OR DESCRIPTION OF DEPOSIT	(-) AMOUNT OF CHECK	√T	(+) AMOUNT OF DEPOSIT	BALANCE 275 16
346	8-3	Joe's Market (groceries)	41 76			
347	8-10	Samantha's Swim Shop (beach wear)	62 43			

12.

CHECK NO	DATE	CHECKS ISSUED TO OR DESCRIPTION OF DEPOSIT	(-) AMOUNT OF CHECK	√T	(+) AMOUNT OF DEPOSIT	BALANCE 642 37
211	9-10	Ye Olde Bake Shop (birthday cake)	35 19			
Deposit	9-21	Paycheck			371 00	

13.

CHECK NO	DATE	CHECKS ISSUED TO OR DESCRIPTION OF DEPOSIT	(-) AMOUNT OF CHECK	√T	(+) AMOUNT OF DEPOSIT	BALANCE 135 71
Deposit	4-3	Cash			100 00	
721	4-7	Valley Power and Light (electric bill)	47 21			

CHAPTER

PLANNING A TRIP

USING BASIC MATH SKILLS TO SOLVE PROBLEMS RELATED TO TRAVEL.

KEY WORDS:

1. **Arrival Time:** time of reaching your destination.
2. **Departure Time:** time of leaving on a trip.
3. **Elapsed Time:** the amount of time that passes between departure and arrival.
4. **Estimate:** a guess as close as possible to the actual cost.
5. **Fare:** the price of riding on public transportation.
6. **Key:** part of a map that tells what different symbols mean.
7. **Round Trip:** a trip from one place to another and back.

The Arithmians are spending a quiet evening at home and decide that they should begin traveling to see the rest of the country. In Arithmia they always planned their trips using interstellar path finding. Anja finds the Americans use road maps to plan trips, so she learns exactly how to use them. She begins to show Ranzo and Miro how to use a road map.

She tells them that the numbers in circles, ovals, and shields name the highways and roads; the small *uncircled* numbers next to the roads will tell them how far they'll have to travel to get from one town to the next. Since people usually like to go the shortest distance possible, these numbers are very useful.

SKILL: Finding the distance between cities using a road map.

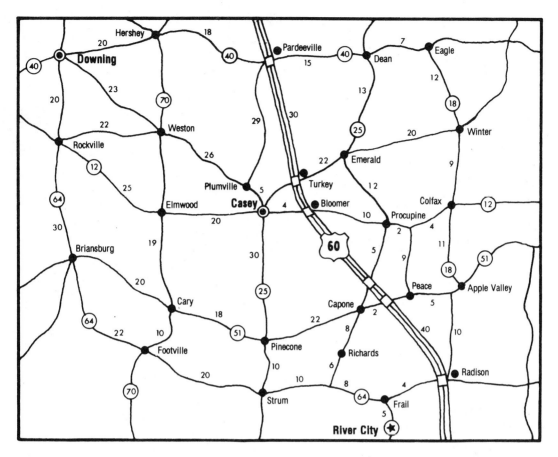

1. Find the town of Eagle.

2. Find the town of Winter. There's a road between Eagle and Winter called Highway 18. You know it's a highway because it's circled. The small number, 12, tells how far it is between the two towns.

First, the three Arithmians try this way: from River City up to Frail; from Frail to Radison; then north on Highway 60 through Bloomer to Pardeeville; from Pardeeville to Hershey, and then on to Downing. Next, they decide to write down the planned route, with the miles, and then add to find the total number of miles.

River City to Frail	5	Miles
Frail to Radison	4	Miles
Radison to Bloomer	40	Miles
Bloomer to Pardeeville	30	Miles
Pardeeville to Hershey	18	Miles
Hershey to Downing	20	Miles
TOTAL	117	Miles

SAMPLE:

River City to Frail	5	Miles
Frail to Strum	18	Miles
Strum to Footville	20	Miles
Footville to Brainsburg	22	Miles
Brainsburg to Rockville	30	Miles
Rockville to Downing	20	Miles
TOTAL	115	Miles

ANJA'S WAY	
River City to Frail	_____ Miles
Frail to Strum	_____ Miles
Strum to Pinecone	_____ Miles
Pinecone to Casey	_____ Miles
Casey to Elmwood	_____ Miles
Elmwood to Rockville	_____ Miles
Rockville to Downing	_____ Miles
TOTAL	_____ Miles

RANZO'S WAY	
River City to Frail	_____ Miles
Frail to Radison	_____ Miles
Radison to Bloomer	_____ Miles
Bloomer to Casey	_____ Miles
Casey to Plumville	_____ Miles
Plumville to Weston	_____ Miles
Weston to Downing	_____ Miles
TOTAL	_____ Miles

1. Who chose the shortest route?

2. Who chose the longest route?

3. What is the difference in miles between the shortest route and the longest route?

Use this map to figure out how many miles it would take to travel each of the following routes.

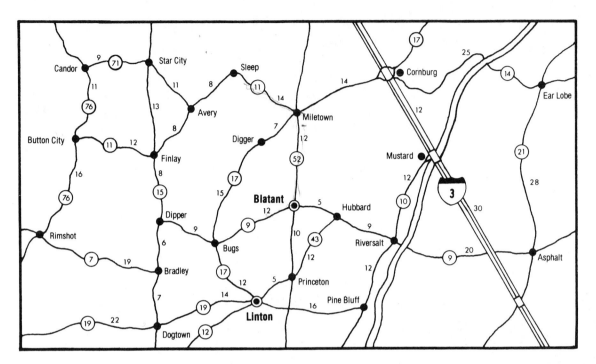

SAMPLE:

You want to go from Blatant to Candor. The route you choose is Blatant to Bugs; Bugs to Dipper; Dipper to Finlay; Finlay to Button City; Button City to Candor.

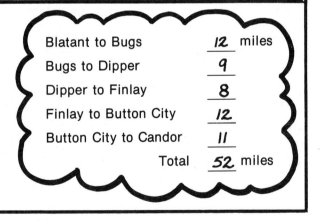

Blatant to Bugs	*12* miles
Bugs to Dipper	*9*
Dipper to Finlay	*8*
Finlay to Button City	*12*
Button City to Candor	*11*
Total	*52* miles

√ 1. **Blatant to Candor**
Blatant to Miletown to
Sleep to Avery to
Star City to Candor
Total miles_____

2. **Cornburg to Linton**
Cornburg to Mustard to
Riversalt to Hubbard
to Princeton to Linton
Total miles_____

3. **Cornburg to Linton**
Cornburg to Miletown
to Blatant to Princeton
to Linton
Total miles_____

4. **Bradley to Earlobe**
   Bradley to Dipper to
   Bugs to Digger to
   Miletown to Cornburg
   to Earlobe
   Total miles_____

5. **Bradley to Earlobe**
   Bradley to Dipper to
   Finlay to Avery to
   Sleep to Miletown to
   Cornburg to Earlobe
   Total miles_____

6. **Bradley to Earlobe**
   Bradley to Dogtown to
   Linton to Pine Bluff to
   Riversalt to Asphalt to
   Earlobe
   Total miles_____

Use the total mileage from these six problems and the practice problem to find the correct answers to the following three questions.

7. What is the shortest way to get from Blatant to Candor?
   (a) through Bugs and Dipper
   (b) through Miletown and Sleep City

8. What is the shortest way to get from Cornburg to Linton?
   (a) through Mustard and Riversalt
   (b) through Miletown and Blatant

9. What is the shortest way to get from Bradley to Earlobe?
   (a) through Bugs and Digger
   (b) through Finlay and Avery
   (c) through Dogtown and Linton

Use the map on page 204 to answer the next two questions.

10. What Is the shortest way to get from Miletown to Asphalt?
    (a) through Cornburg and Riversalt
    (b) through Blatant and Hubbard
    (c) through Cornburg and Earlobe

11. What is the shortest way to get from Linton to Sleep?
    (a) through Bugs and Digger
    (b) through Dipper and Finlay
    (c) through Princeton and Blatant

For more practice in calculating mileage, use the map below to figure out how many miles it would take to travel each route. Do your work on a separate sheet of paper.

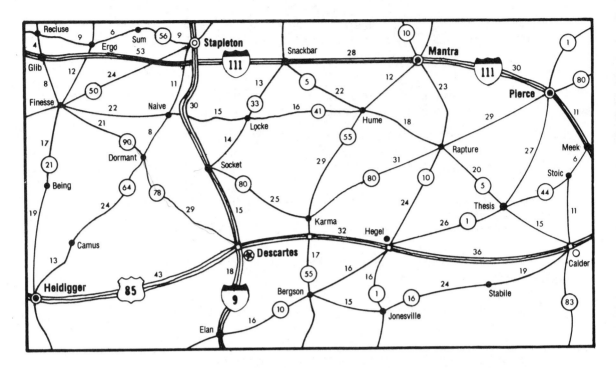

1. **Descartes to Recluse**
   Descartes to Dormant   —
   to Finesse   —
   to Glib   —
   to Recluse   —
   Total miles   —

2. **Calder to Mantra**
   Calder to Stoic   —
   to Meek   —
   to Pierce   —
   to Mantra   —
   Total miles   —

3. **Calder to Mantra**
   Calder to Thesis   —
   to Rapture   —
   to Hume   —
   to Mantra   —
   Total miles   —

4. **Heidigger to Locke**
   Heidigger to Camus   —
   to Dormant   —
   to Naive   —
   to Locke   —
   Total miles   —

5. **Heidigger to Locke**
   Heidigger to Descartes   —
   to Socket   —
   to Locke   —
   Total miles   —

6. **Heidigger to Locke**
   Heidigger to Being   —
   to Finesse   —
   to Naive   —
   to Locke   —
   Total miles   —

Use the total mileage from these six problems to find the correct answers to the following three questions.

7. What is the shortest way to get from Descartes to Recluse?
   (a) through Socket
   (b) through Dormant

Planning a Trip

8. What is the shortest way to get from Calder to Mantra?
   (a) through Stoic and Meek
   (b) through Thesis and Rapture

9. Which problem above shows the longest route from Heidigger to Locke?
   (a) problem 4
   (b) problem 5
   (c) problem 6

Use the map on page 206 to answer the next three questions.

10. Which is the shortest route from Pierce to Karma?
    (a) Highway 80
    (b) Highways 111 and 55

11. Which is the shortest route from Bergson to Calder?
    (a) through Jonesville and Stabile
    (b) through Hegel

12. Which is the shortest route from Snackbar to Jonesville?
    (a) Take Highway 5 to Rapture. Go south on Highway 10 to Hegel and take Highway 1 to Jonesville.
    (b) Take Highway 5 to Hume. Go south on Highway 55 to Bergson, then go east on Highway 16 to Jonesville.

The KEY on the next page tells what each of the map symbols mean. Look carefully at the key. Use it to answer the following questions.

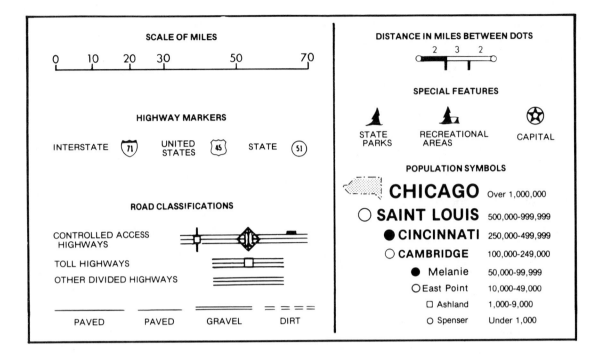

1. What does this symbol mean?
   (a) capital
   (b) highway marker
   (c) state park

2. If a city is marked ◯ , how many people live there?
   (a) about 400
   (b) 10,000 to 20,000
   (c) over 500,000

3. What kind of highway does this marker show? ⑭
   (a) interstate highway
   (b) U.S. highway
   (c) state highway

4. What kind of road does this line indicate? ═══
   (a) paved road
   (b) divided highway
   (c) dirt road

Miro is going to borrow a friend's car for their trip. Ranzo thinks that they can travel free with a car, but he has forgotten about the gas and oil. Anja explains to him how to figure out how much it will cost to travel in a car.

SAMPLE:

Number of miles since last fill-up on gas   <u>300</u> miles

Gallons needed for a fill-up now   <u>20</u> gallons

Miles per gallon   <u>15</u> m.p.g.

Divide the number of miles by the number of gallons

$$\begin{array}{r} 15 \\ 20\overline{)300} \\ \underline{20} \\ 100 \\ \underline{100} \end{array}$$

Now figure the m.p.g. (miles per gallon) for these problems. Round to the nearest gallon when necessary.

√ 1. Number of miles since last fill-up of gas   405
   Gallons needed for a fill-up now   25
   Miles per gallon   _____

√ 2. Number of miles since last fill-up of gas   214
   Gallons needed for a fill-up now   24
   Miles per gallon   _____

3. Number of miles since last fill-up of gas   440
   Gallons needed for a fill-up now   11
   Miles per gallon   _____

4. Number of miles since last fill-up of gas   235
   Gallons needed for a fill-up now   22
   Miles per gallon   _____

5. Number of miles since last fill-up of gas   183
   Gallons needed for a fill-up now   15
   Miles per gallon   _____

6. Number of miles since last fill-up of gas   32
   Gallons needed for a fill-up now   5
   Miles per gallon   _____

7. Number of miles since last fill-up of gas: 297
   Gallons needed for a fill-up now   10
   Miles per gallon   _____

For more practice in figuring m.p.g. (miles per gallon), solve the following problems.

1. Number of miles since last fill-up of gas   252
   Gallons needed for a fill-up now   14
   Miles per gallon   _____

2. Number of miles since last fill-up of gas   529
   Gallons needed for a fill-up now   23
   Miles per gallon   _____

3. Number of miles since last fill-up of gas   221
   Gallons needed for a fill-up now   13
   Miles per gallon   _____

4. Number of miles since last fill-up of gas   37
   Gallons needed for a fill-up now   3
   Miles per gallon   _____

5. Number of miles since last fill-up of gas   567
   Gallons needed for a fill-up now   15
   Miles per gallon   _____

6. Number of miles since last fill-up of gas   183
   Gallons needed for a fill-up now   15
   Miles per gallon   _____

SKILL: Figuring *elapsed time.*

1. Departure Time: This is the time you would *leave* on the trip.
2. Arrival Time:　　This is the time you would get where you're going.

Planning a Trip

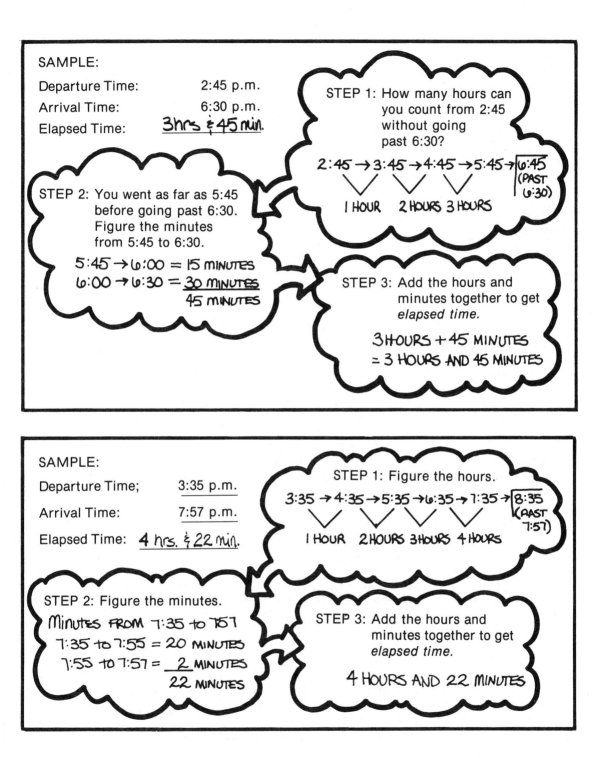

SAMPLE:

Departure Time: 2:45 p.m.

Arrival Time: 6:30 p.m.

Elapsed Time: 3 hrs & 45 min.

STEP 1: How many hours can you count from 2:45 without going past 6:30?

2:45 → 3:45 → 4:45 → 5:45 → 6:45 (PAST 6:30)

1 HOUR   2 HOURS   3 HOURS

STEP 2: You went as far as 5:45 before going past 6:30. Figure the minutes from 5:45 to 6:30.

5:45 → 6:00 = 15 MINUTES
6:00 → 6:30 = 30 MINUTES
              45 MINUTES

STEP 3: Add the hours and minutes together to get *elapsed time.*

3 HOURS + 45 MINUTES
= 3 HOURS AND 45 MINUTES

SAMPLE:

Departure Time; 3:35 p.m.

Arrival Time: 7:57 p.m.

Elapsed Time: 4 hrs. & 22 min.

STEP 1: Figure the hours.

3:35 → 4:35 → 5:35 → 6:35 → 7:35 → 8:35 (PAST 7:57)

1 HOUR   2 HOURS   3 HOURS   4 HOURS

STEP 2: Figure the minutes.

Minutes FROM 7:35 to 7:57
7:35 to 7:55 = 20 MINUTES
7:55 to 7:57 = 2 MINUTES
               22 MINUTES

STEP 3: Add the hours and minutes together to get *elapsed time.*

4 HOURS AND 22 MINUTES

In each problem below, there is a departure time and an arrival time. You need to figure out the *elapsed time.* First find the number of hours, then the number of minutes, as shown in the samples.

✓1. Departure time: 12:00 noon
   Arrival time: 7:15 pm
   Elapsed time _____

✓2. Departure time: 1:15 am
   Arrival time: 1:30 pm
   Elapsed time _____

3. Departure time: 11:00 am
   Arrival time: 9:37 pm
   Elapsed time _____

4. Departure time: 4:31 am
   Arrival time: 1:00 pm
   Elapsed time _____

5. Departure time: 1:30 pm
   Arrival time: 6:27 pm
   Elapsed time _____

6. Departure time: 3:15 am
   Arrival time: 11:00 am
   Elapsed time _____

7. Departure time: 8:00 pm
   Arrival time: 3:08 am
   Elapsed time _____

8. Departure time: 9:47 am
   Arrival time: 4:45 pm
   Elapsed time _____

For additional practice in calculating elapsed time, solve the four following problems.

1. Departure time: 7:00 am
   Arrival time: 2:30 pm
   Elapsed time _____

2. Departure time: 1:00 pm
   Arrival time: 9:20 pm
   Elapsed time _____

3. Departure time: 5:25 pm
   Arrival time: 3:05 am
   Elapsed time _____

4. Departure time: 10:15 am
   Arrival time: 11:50 pm
   Elapsed time _____

SKILL: Identifying the most appropriate way to travel for a certain kind of trip.

RANZO, IF YOU TAKE THE TRAIN TO MEET US IN DOWNING, HOW MUCH WILL IT COST?

GOSH! I DON'T KNOW. I DIDN'T THINK OF THAT! HOW CAN I FIND OUT?

Planning a Trip

AUTOMOBILE:
   a. The cheapest way to travel is to drive a car. (This may be changing with the rising cost of gasoline.)
   b. On long trips, you'll have to pay for meals and hotel rooms.
   c. There *may* be tolls or car repairs that will make the trip more expensive.
   d. Travel by car allows you to stop wherever you like and take side trips that may seem interesting.

AIRPLANE:
   a. Usually the most expensive way to travel is to fly.
   b. Flying is the fastest way to travel.
   c. Meals served on the plane are usually included in the ticket price.
   d. Flying is the best way to go if you have no time or desire to sightsee.
   e. You will probably have to arrange other transportation to get to and from the airport.

TRAIN:
   a. Travel by train usually costs less than flying, but the trip takes longer.
   b. Many trains have dining cars where meals are served.

c. There are sleeping accommodations on the train for trips that take more than one day, but they cost more.

d. Riding on the train gives you the chance to see a lot of scenery, but you can't take side trips or stop to enjoy certain interesting places.

e. There are many cities in the Unites States that are not served by passenger trains.

f. You may have to arrange other transportation to get to and from the train station.

BUS:

a. Usually, the cheapest way to travel, other than by car, is the bus.

b. Buses travel to nearly every city in the United States.

c. Because they stop so often, it may take you a long time to get where you are going.

d. You have a chance to take in a lot of scenery.

e. Special arrangements can be made so you can get on and off the bus as many times as you like during a certain period of time; this allows you to visit sites of special interest.

Use the comments above to decide the best way to travel on each of the following trips.

√ 1. Angela wants to travel to Los Angeles, California to interview for a job with an important politician. She only has about 4 days to get there and back. And she lives more than 2,000 miles away! The politician told Angela that he would pay for all of Angela's travel expenses.

(a) drive a car   (b) ride the bus   (c) ride the train   (d) fly

2. Miro wants to see what it is like outside the city where he lives. He can't drive a car and he's afraid to stop in little towns where people might notice that he's a Arithmian. The idea of eating in restaurants especially frightens him. He'd like to travel into the country without having actually to walk around the country.

(a) ride the bus   (b) ride the train   (c) fly

3. Eric has two weeks off from work next month. He'd like to get out into the country and see the sights. The trouble is, he doesn't have much money. And he doesn't like to have anyone else plan the route he takes. More than anything Eric wants the chance to get on back roads that are rarely traveled.

(a) drive a car   (b) ride the bus   (c) ride the train   (d) fly

4. Simon and Trudy want to visit an enormous fantasy land that they heard about in Florida. They've saved a lot of money for the trip, but they have only about a week to get there, see the sights, and come home again. And they're a thousand miles away from Florida and the place they want to visit!

(a) drive a car   (b) ride the bus   (c) ride the train   (d) fly

5. Ranzo is determined to learn more about Earthlings. He thinks it would help if he had a chance to travel and meet a lot of different people from big cities and small towns. He would also like to see what different towns and cities are like in America. Ranzo has about 3 weeks to travel.

(a) drive a car   (b) ride the bus   (c) ride the train   (d) fly

     Planning a Trip

1. *Transportation:* If plane, bus, or train, how much will the ticket cost?

2. *Food:* Will you be eating in expensive restaurants?

3. *Lodging:* Will you be staying in expensive hotels? Small motor inns? Will you be staying with friends, at no cost?

4. *Entertainment:* What will you be doing to have fun? Will it cost much?

5. *Special Admission Fees:* Will you be going to shows, museums, concerts, or other places that charge admission?

6. *Shopping:* Will you be buying gifts or souvenirs?

7. *Emergencies:* What if something goes wrong? How much extra money will you have to get out of a jam?

YOU SHOULD ESTIMATE THE COST OF THE TRIP SOMETHING LIKE THIS:

SAMPLE:

You are going to visit the city of Muka-Puka about 700 miles away. You don't have time to drive since you only have 4 days for vacation. Instead, you'll fly. A round trip ticket will cost you $125. That way you can arrive on Friday, stay in a hotel Friday night, Saturday night, and Sunday night.

On Monday, you can fly home again. It will cost about $25 to get back and forth to the airport, and about $30 for taxi fares around Muka-Puka. The hotel rate is $37 per night. Food will be expensive at the hotel, so you'll eat at a small cafe down the street for only $8 on Friday night, $15 per day on Saturday and Sunday, and $5 on Monday morning.

There are two concerts you want to see. One costs $9.50, and the other costs $8.50. You'll also spend about $50 just having fun. You might buy a present for a special friend while you're in town, so you'd better hang on to $20 for that. If anything goes wrong, you have $50 hidden in the toe of your shoe. Have fun!

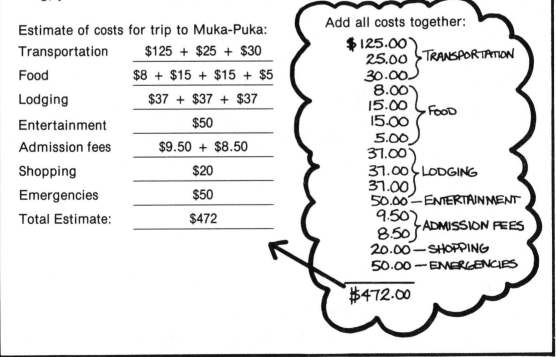

Estimate of costs for trip to Muka-Puka:

Transportation	$125 + $25 + $30
Food	$8 + $15 + $15 + $5
Lodging	$37 + $37 + $37
Entertainment	$50
Admission fees	$9.50 + $8.50
Shopping	$20
Emergencies	$50
Total Estimate:	$472

Add all costs together:

$ 125.00 ⎫
25.00 ⎬ TRANSPORTATION
30.00 ⎭
8.00 ⎫
15.00 ⎪
15.00 ⎬ FOOD
5.00 ⎭
37.00 ⎫
37.00 ⎬ LODGING
37.00 ⎭
50.00 — ENTERTAINMENT
9.50 ⎫
8.50 ⎭ ADMISSION FEES
20.00 — SHOPPING
50.00 — EMERGENCIES
_____
$472.00

Read each of the following vacation plans. Find the total estimated costs for taking these trips.

✓1. Get ready for a great time! You're going to take a tour of the Southwest. A special bus ticket allows you to travel all you want during your 15 day vacation. The ticket costs $150.00. The great thing is, you can get on and off the bus as many times as you like! You'll spend a day or two in several small western towns. Count on spending about 11 nights in small hotels. (The other 4 nights you can spend with friends.) You'll pay $13 each night. You can eat out about half the time and make sandwiches the rest of the time. This will bring your food bill down to about $6 a day. Entertainment is high on your list. You'll spend an average of $5 a day just having fun. And whenever you get the chance, you'll visit museums, caves, forts, or any interesting site. Save about $55 for admission fees. Every place you stop will have some sort of souvenir stand. You'll spend about $30 on souvenirs and gifts. Just in case an emergency comes up, you'll have $35 tucked away in your suitcase.

ESTIMATE OF COSTS FOR TOUR OF THE SOUTHWEST

Transportation _____   Admission Fees _____
Food _____   Shopping _____
Lodging _____   Emergencies _____
Entertainment_____

Total Estimate _____

2. What news! Your long lost third cousin, Ferdinand, whom you haven't seen for 10 years, called you on the phone. He said he's visiting in the nearby town of Centerville, 35 miles away. He said you should get there fast because he's only staying one day. You haven't got a car so you'll have to rent one. The car rental company charges a flat fee of $10 per day and 10¢ for every mile you drive. For the one day you'll have the car, you'll drive 100 miles. But don't forget the gas! Better plan on buying 7 gallons at an average cost of $1.89 per gallon. And don't forget, *you're* going to pay for lunch. You want to treat Ferdinand to a fancy meal, one that will cost about $25 for the two of you. Plan on getting back home too tired to cook your own supper. Eat out at the corner Hardly Burgers for $1.25.

ESTIMATE OF COSTS FOR TRIP TO CENTERVILLE

Transportation _____   Admission Fees _____
Food _____   Shopping _____
Lodging _____   Emergencies _____
Entertainment_____

Total Estimate _____

3. Congratulations!! You have won a one week vacation at the Gordon Nelson Motel in beautiful Kenosha, Wisconsin! The prize includes all meals and pays for the motel room. You must pay all transportation costs and any extra costs. You have decided to take the train, since you have never traveled on one before. Train fare will cost $155.00 round trip. On the train, you'll have to buy your own food. The trip takes about 8 hours, so you'll eat lunch and dinner in the dining car. Lunches cost $3.50 and dinner costs $7.00. (Don't forget: you must also buy these meals on the trip home.) The train will let you off in Racine. From there, you'll take a bus to Kenosha. Bus fare is $7.50 one way. The bus takes you right to the Gordon Nelson Motel. Take along about $100 for entertainment and $75 for emergencies. You should also figure on spending about $50 for gifts and souvenirs.

ESTIMATE OF COSTS FOR A TRIP TO KENOSHA, WISCONSIN

Transportation _____   Admission Fees _____

Food_____   Shopping _____

Lodging _____   Emergencies _____

Entertainment _____

Total Estimate _____

Chapter 8
Self-Test

For items 1-4, use the map below. Follow the shortest route each time. (See pages 200-207)

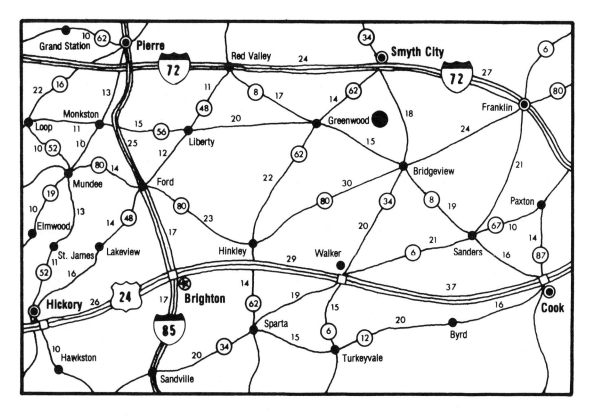

1. How many miles between Red Valley and Turkeyvale?

2. How many miles between Ford and Franklin?

3. How many miles between Hickory and Paxton?

4. How many miles between Liberty and Cook?

For items 5-6, determine the number of miles driven per gallon. (See pages 209-211.)

5. Number of miles since last fill-up: _____323_____
   Number of gallons required for fill-up now: _____19_____
   How many m.p.g. (miles per gallon)? _____

6. Number of miles since last fill-up: _____280_____
   Number of gallons required for fill-up now: _____8_____
   How many m.p.g. (miles per gallon)? _____

For items 7-9, determine the elapsed time between departure and arrival. (See pages 211-214.)

7. Departure time: 10:00 am
   Arrival time: 3:30 pm

8. Departure time: 5:15 pm
   Arrival time: 8:30 pm

9. Departure time: 8:50 pm
   Arrival time: 11:10 pm

For items 10-11, decide which is the best way to travel on each trip — to drive, to take a train, to take a bus, or to fly. (See pages 214-216.)

10. Howard wants to go home for his brother's birthday. His problem is that he lives about 1000 miles from his brother, and he can only miss two days of work.

11. Lynn has never seen an ocean. She wants to take a trip to California to see the Pacific Ocean. On the way she would like to see many of the interesting sights of the beautiful countryside. Lynn has 3 weeks vacation, so time is not a problem, but she would like to travel as cheaply as possible.

For item 12, figure out how much money is needed to take the trip described. (See pages 217-220.)

12. You are going to visit your grandmother in a distant city. You have decided to take a train; your round trip ticket costs $219. A taxi will take you to and from the train station for $35. Your grandmother insists you will stay at her house and drive her car while you visit, so lodging and transportation are no problem. Also, Grandma is a fantastic cook so you'll be eating many meals at home with her. You do want to get flowers for her when you arrive at the train station, and they will be about $10. In addition, there are two fancy restaurants in town; Grandma would love being treated to meals there, which will cost you about $40 in each restaurant. Of course, before you leave you want to buy your grandmother a present for around $25. Don't forget to take another $50 for emergencies. How much money will you need for this trip?

Planning a Trip

TAX TIME!

USING BASIC MATH SKILLS TO SOLVE PROBLEMS RELATED TO TAXES.

KEY WORDS:

1. **1040:** an income tax return. It is often called the *long form.*

2. **1040A:** an income tax return. It is often called the *short form.*

3. **Adjusted Gross Income:** when you file an income tax return, you figure the tax you owe on the amount of your *adjusted gross income.* This amount is figured by adding all your income and then subtracting all deductions allowed by the government.

4. **Deduction:** the amount of money you can subtract from your income for certain expenses. You don't have to pay income tax on the money you are allowed to deduct.

5. **Exemption:** a set amount of money which you may deduct for each person, including yourself, who depends on your income.

6. **Federal Withholding Tax:** the tax your employer takes out of your pay and sends to the government. Your withholding tax goes toward paying off the income tax you owe.

7. **Gasoline Tax Rate Table:** a chart you use to figure how much you can deduct on your income tax for the gasoline tax you paid during the year.

8. **Income Tax:** a tax the government collects from almost every working citizen. The U.S. and most state governments collect income taxes.

9. **Income Tax Return:** a form you fill out to figure how much income tax you owe.

10. **Income Tax Table:** a chart you use to find the amount of income tax you owe.

11. **Itemizing Deductions:** listing the amounts of money spent on such things as medical bills and state taxes. You do this only when filing a 1040 income tax return.

12. **Rate of Tax:** the percentage of an amount you pay for tax. A 6% tax is a 6% rate of tax.

13. **Sales Tax:** a tax you pay on goods you buy. A sales tax is always expressed as a percent—for example, a 3% sales tax. The sales tax which people pay is collected and sent to a state or city government.

14. **Sales Tax Table:** a chart showing how much sales tax is owed on purchases.

15. **Subtotal:** the sum of purchases you've made before tax is added.

SKILL: Figuring sales tax on purchases by using a tax table.

Miro is very excited because he has learned how to use a *sales tax table* at work. Anja and Ranzo are anxious to learn now, too.

6% SALES TAX TABLE

Sale Amount	Tax	Sale Amount	Tax	Sale Amount	Tax	Sale Amount	Tax
$ .00— .10	None	$2.35—2.50	.15	$5.11—5.17	.31	$7.68— 7.84	.47
.11— .17	.01	2.51—2.67	.16	5.18—5.34	.32	7.85— 8.10	.48
.18— .34	.02	2.68—2.84	.17	5.35—5.50	.33	8.11— 8.17	.49
.35— .50	.03	2.85—3.10	.18	5.51—5.67	.34	8.18— 8.34	.50
.51— .67	.04	3.11—3.17	.19	5.68—5.84	.35	8.35— 8.50	.51
.68— .84	.05	3.18—3.34	.20	5.85—6.10	.36	8.51— 8.67	.52
.85—1.10	.06	3.35—3.50	.21	6.11—6.17	.37	8.68— 8.84	.53
1.11—1.17	.07	3.51—3.67	.22	6.18—6.34	.38	8.85— 9.10	.54
1.18—1.34	.08	3.68—3.84	.23	6.35—6.50	.39	9.11— 9.17	.55
1.35—1.50	.09	3.85—4.10	.24	6.51—6.67	.40	9.18— 9.34	.56
1.51—1.67	.10	4.11—4.17	.25	6.68—6.84	.41	9.35— 9.50	.57
1.68—1.84	.11	4.18—4.34	.26	6.85—7.10	.42	9.51— 9.67	.58
1.85—2.10	.12	4.35—4.50	.27	7.11—7.17	.43	9.68— 9.84	.59
2.11—2.17	.13	4.51—4.67	.28	7.18—7.34	.44	9.85—10.00	.60
2.18—2.34	.14	4.68—4.84	.29	7.35—7.50	.45		
		4.85—5.10	.30	7.51—7.67	.46		

THIS IS EASY! AND YOU SPENT ALL DAY LEARNING HOW TO DO THIS ?
WELL, THERE IS MORE TO IT. LIKE WHAT WOULD YOU DO IF YOU RANG UP AN AMOUNT THAT ISN'T ON THE TAX TABLE.
YOU SEE, THIS TAX TABLE ONLY GOES UP TO $10.00.
ER-EH-UM!??
THAT'S WHAT I THOUGHT. IF YOU WANT TO FIND THE TAX ON A SUBTOTAL OF $36.07, YOU'LL HAVE TO...

...LOOK ON THE CHART AND FIND THE TAX FOR $10.00
WHAT YOU WANT TO FIGURE IS HOW MANY TIMES YOU HAVE $10.00 IN THE $36. DON'T WORRY ABOUT THE 7¢ YET.

Sale Amount	Tax
$9.51 - $ 9.67	$.58
9.68 - 9.84	.59
9.85 - 10.00	.60

SAMPLE:

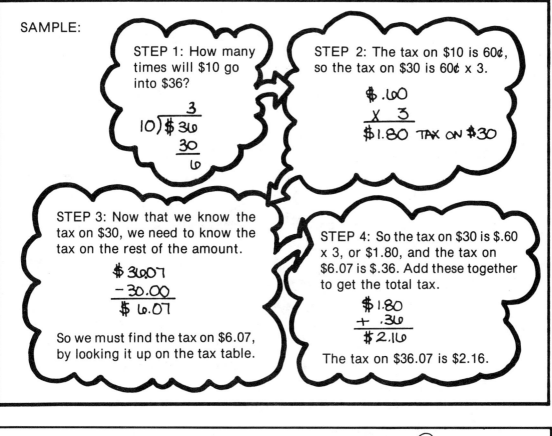

STEP 1: How many times will $10 go into $36?

$$10)\overline{\$36}$$ with quotient 3, $\underline{30}$, remainder 6

STEP 2: The tax on $10 is 60¢, so the tax on $30 is 60¢ x 3.

$$\begin{array}{r} \$.60 \\ \times\ 3 \\ \hline \$1.80 \end{array}$$ TAX ON $30

STEP 3: Now that we know the tax on $30, we need to know the tax on the rest of the amount.

$$\begin{array}{r} \$36.07 \\ -30.00 \\ \hline \$6.07 \end{array}$$

So we must find the tax on $6.07, by looking it up on the tax table.

STEP 4: So the tax on $30 is $.60 x 3, or $1.80, and the tax on $6.07 is $.36. Add these together to get the total tax.

$$\begin{array}{r} \$1.80 \\ +\ .36 \\ \hline \$2.16 \end{array}$$

The tax on $36.07 is $2.16.

HERE'S ANOTHER SAMPLE FOR YOU TO TRY.

SAMPLE: Find the tax on $28.57.

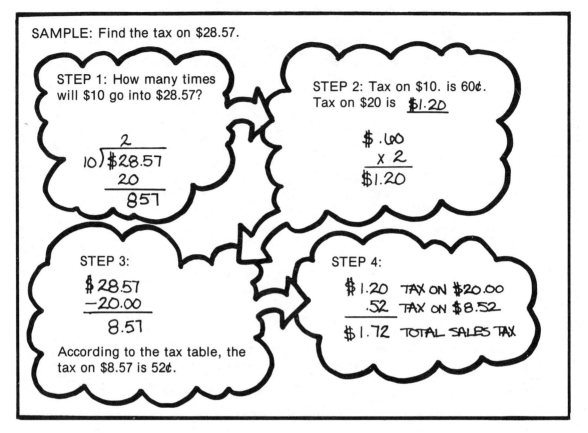

STEP 1: How many times will $10 go into $28.57?

$$10\overline{)\begin{array}{r}2\\ \$28.57\\ 20\\ \hline 857\end{array}}$$

STEP 2: Tax on $10. is 60¢. Tax on $20 is $1.20

$$\begin{array}{r}\$.60\\ \times\ 2\\ \hline \$1.20\end{array}$$

STEP 3:

$$\begin{array}{r}\$28.57\\ -20.00\\ \hline 8.51\end{array}$$

According to the tax table, the tax on $8.57 is 52¢.

STEP 4:

$$\begin{array}{rl}\$1.20 & \text{TAX ON }\$20.00\\ .52 & \text{TAX ON }\$8.52\\ \hline \$1.72 & \text{TOTAL SALES TAX}\end{array}$$

Use the "6% Sales Tax Table" on page 225 to find the proper amount of tax for the SUBTOTAL shown on each of the following bills, and then add the SUBTOTAL and the TAX to determine the TOTAL.

✓ 1.

Subtotal	6	93
Tax		
Total		

✓ 2.

Subtotal	15	98
Tax		
Total		

3.

Subtotal	1	75
Tax		
Total		

4.

Subtotal	10	52
Tax		
Total		

5.

Subtotal	37	94
Tax		
Total		

6.

Subtotal	106	52
Tax		
Total		

Tax Time!

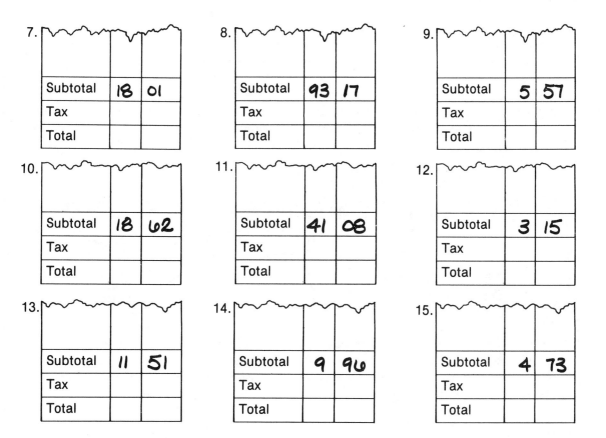

7.

Subtotal	18	01
Tax		
Total		

8.

Subtotal	93	17
Tax		
Total		

9.

Subtotal	5	57
Tax		
Total		

10.

Subtotal	18	62
Tax		
Total		

11.

Subtotal	41	08
Tax		
Total		

12.

Subtotal	3	15
Tax		
Total		

13.

Subtotal	11	51
Tax		
Total		

14.

Subtotal	9	96
Tax		
Total		

15.

Subtotal	4	73
Tax		
Total		

Complete each of the following bills. First, add the purchases to get a SUBTOTAL. Then, find the tax by using the "6% Sales Tax Table" on page 225. Finally, add the SUBTOTAL and TAX to get the TOTAL.

1.

shoes	18	63
skirt	19	41
Subtotal		
Tax		
Total		

2.

pen	3	04
paper	7	01
Subtotal		
Tax		
Total		

3.

bott		18
scraper	4	31
brush	1	52
Subtotal		
Tax		
Total		

4.

repairs	53	84
Subtotal		
Tax		
Total		

5.

gloves	7	63
hat	1	05
one sock		86
Subtotal		
Tax		
Total		

6.

glasses	19	28
stapler	13	62
cup		84
Subtotal		
Tax		
Total		

Learning all about sales taxes makes the Arithmians interested in the other taxes Americans pay. Anja does a lot of research about *Income Tax.* She finds that every year, the U.S. government collects an income tax from almost every person who earns money. Almost everybody pays income tax, but not everybody pays the same *amount* of income tax.

HOW MUCH MONEY YOU EARN MAKES A BIG DIFFERENCE IN HOW MUCH **INCOME TAX** YOU PAY.

USUALLY, THE MORE YOU EARN, THE MORE INCOME TAX YOU PAY.

How much you pay in income tax also depends on the *rate of tax* you pay. People who are single, for example, pay a little higher tax than married people do. You owe income tax on the money you earn in a year. You pay this income tax only a little bit at a time.

REMEMBER WHEN YOU GOT YOUR FIRST JOB AND YOU LEARNED ABOUT YOUR **PAYCHECK STUB** ?

SURE. THERE WAS A **DEDUCTION** FOR **FEDERAL WITHHOLDING TAX**.

THE **FEDERAL** WITHHOLDING TAX IS THE MONEY TAKEN OUT OF YOUR CHECK TO PAY THE **INCOME TAX**. IT IS **WITHHELD** OR **KEPT** FROM YOUR PAYCHECK.

HOW DO OUR BOSSES KNOW HOW MUCH MONEY TO WITHHOLD ?

WHEN YOU WERE HIRED FOR YOUR JOB, YOU FILLED OUT A FORM CALLED **W-4**.

The total amount of *withholding tax* taken out of your pay is hardly ever the *exact* amount of money you owe for income taxes. At the end of the year, you have to figure out if you've paid exactly what you owe.

The government provides free 1040 and 1040A instruction booklets every year to help you fill out your tax return. Either of these booklets will help you decide which return you ought to fill out.

Your teacher will give you a Form 1040A tax return and instructions on how to fill out this form. Follow the instructions step-by-step to fill out the form. Assume you are filling it out for a taxpayer named Al Q. Taxpayer. Your teacher may want you to choose a partner with whom to work. In the following box you will find all the information you need about Al Q. Taxpayer to start to fill out the form. *Stop* after you complete Item 13, then show it to your teacher.

Who he is and where he lives:

AL Q. TAXPAYER
7 Dullsville Lane
River City, Indiana 20202

I Sell Anything

(515) 369-8405

His Social Security number:

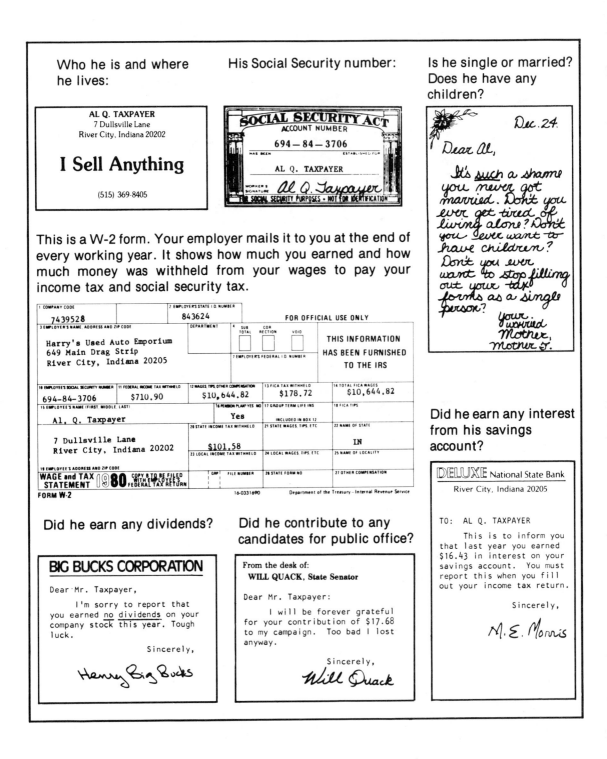

SOCIAL SECURITY ACT
ACCOUNT NUMBER
694 — 84 — 3706
HAS BEEN   ESTABLISHED FOR

AL Q. TAXPAYER

WORKER'S SIGNATURE *Al Q. Taxpayer*

FOR SOCIAL SECURITY PURPOSES - NOT FOR IDENTIFICATION

Is he single or married? Does he have any children?

Dec. 24.

Dear Al,

It's such a shame you never got married. Don't you ever get tired of living alone? Don't you ever want to have children? Don't you ever want to stop filling out your tax forms as a single person?

Your worried Mother, Mother J.

This is a W-2 form. Your employer mails it to you at the end of every working year. It shows how much you earned and how much money was withheld from your wages to pay your income tax and social security tax.

1 COMPANY CODE		2 EMPLOYER'S STATE I.D. NUMBER					
7439528		843624			FOR OFFICIAL USE ONLY		
3 EMPLOYER'S NAME, ADDRESS AND ZIP CODE		DEPARTMENT	4 SUB TOTAL	COR RECTION	VOID	THIS INFORMATION	
Harry's Used Auto Emporium 649 Main Drag Strip River City, Indiana 20205						HAS BEEN FURNISHED	
		7 EMPLOYER'S FEDERAL I.D. NUMBER				TO THE IRS	
10 EMPLOYEE'S SOCIAL SECURITY NUMBER	11 FEDERAL INCOME TAX WITHHELD	12 WAGES, TIPS, OTHER COMPENSATION	13 FICA TAX WITHHELD		14 TOTAL FICA WAGES		
694-84-3706	$710.90	$10,644.82	$178.72		$10,644.82		
15 EMPLOYEE'S NAME (FIRST, MIDDLE, LAST)		16 PENSION PLAN YES NO	17 GROUP TERM LIFE INS		18 FICA TIPS		
Al, Q. Taxpayer		Yes	INCLUDED IN BOX 12				
		20 STATE INCOME TAX WITHHELD	21 STATE WAGES, TIPS, ETC	22 NAME OF STATE			
7 Dullsville Lane River City, Indiana 20202		$101.58		IN			
		23 LOCAL INCOME TAX WITHHELD	24 LOCAL WAGES, TIPS, ETC	25 NAME OF LOCALITY			
19 EMPLOYEE'S ADDRESS AND ZIP CODE							
WAGE and TAX STATEMENT 1980 COPY B TO BE FILED WITH EMPLOYEE'S FEDERAL TAX RETURN		GRP FILE NUMBER	26 STATE FORM NO	27 OTHER COMPENSATION			

FORM W-2   16-0331690   Department of the Treasury - Internal Revenue Service

Did he earn any dividends?

BIG BUCKS CORPORATION

Dear Mr. Taxpayer,

I'm sorry to report that you earned <u>no dividends</u> on your company stock this year. Tough luck.

Sincerely,

Henry Big Bucks

Did he contribute to any candidates for public office?

From the desk of:
WILL QUACK, State Senator

Dear Mr. Taxpayer:

I will be forever grateful for your contribution of $17.68 to my campaign. Too bad I lost anyway.

Sincerely,

Will Quack

Did he earn any interest from his savings account?

DELUXE National State Bank
River City, Indiana 20205

TO: AL Q. TAXPAYER

This is to inform you that last year you earned $16.43 in interest on your savings account. You must report this when you fill out your income tax return.

Sincerely,

M. E. Morris

How would you complete lines 9c, 11 and 13 on the following four forms?

√ **1.**

Please Attach Copy B of Forms W–2

7	Wages, salaries, tips, etc. (*Attach Forms W–2. If you do not have a W–2, see page 10 of Instructions*)	7	12,352	98
8	Interest income (*See pages 4 and 10 of Instructions*)	8	157	62
9a	Dividends _____ O (See pages 4 and 10 of Instructions) 9b Exclusion _____ O Subtract line 9b from 9a	9c		
10a	Unemployment compensation. Total amount received ____ O			
b	Taxable part, if any, from worksheet on page 11 of Instructions	10b	O	
11	Adjusted gross income (*add lines 7, 8, 9c, and 10b*). If under $10,000, see page 2 of Instructions on "*Earned Income Credit*"	11		
12a	Credit for contributions to candidates for public office. (*See page 11 of Instructions*) **12a** 10 75			
	IF YOU WANT IRS TO FIGURE YOUR TAX, PLEASE STOP HERE AND SIGN BELOW.			
b	Total Federal income tax withheld (*If line 7 is more than $22,900, see page 12 of Instructions*) **12b** 1750 95			
c	Earned income credit (*from page 2 of Instructions*) . . . . **12c** O			
13	Total (*add lines 12a, b, and c*)	13		

2.

Please Attach Copy B of Forms W–2

7	Wages, salaries, tips, etc. (*Attach Forms W–2. If you do not have a W–2, see page 10 of Instructions*)	7	16,839	58
8	Interest income (*See pages 4 and 10 of Instructions*)	8	343	64
9a	Dividends _____ O (See pages 4 and 10 of Instructions) 9b Exclusion _____ O Subtract line 9b from 9a	9c		
10a	Unemployment compensation. Total amount received ____ O			
b	Taxable part, if any, from worksheet on page 11 of Instructions	10b	O	
11	Adjusted gross income (*add lines 7, 8, 9c, and 10b*). If under $10,000, see page 2 of Instructions on "*Earned Income Credit*"	11		
12a	Credit for contributions to candidates for public office. (*See page 11 of Instructions*) **12a** 25 00			
	IF YOU WANT IRS TO FIGURE YOUR TAX, PLEASE STOP HERE AND SIGN BELOW.			
b	Total Federal income tax withheld (*If line 7 is more than $22,900, see page 12 of Instructions*) **12b** 2955 00			
c	Earned income credit (*from page 2 of Instructions*) . . . . **12c** O			
13	Total (*add lines 12a, b, and c*)	13		

3.

Please Attach Copy B of Forms W–2

7	Wages, salaries, tips, etc. (*Attach Forms W–2. If you do not have a W–2, see page 10 of Instructions*)	7	9833	34
8	Interest income (*See pages 4 and 10 of Instructions*)	8	65	08
9a	Dividends _____ O (See pages 4 and 10 of Instructions) 9b Exclusion _____ O Subtract line 9b from 9a	9c		
10a	Unemployment compensation. Total amount received ____ O			
b	Taxable part, if any, from worksheet on page 11 of Instructions	10b	O	
11	Adjusted gross income (*add lines 7, 8, 9c, and 10b*). If under $10,000, see page 2 of Instructions on "*Earned Income Credit*"	11		
12a	Credit for contributions to candidates for public office. (*See page 11 of Instructions*) . . . . **12a** O			
	IF YOU WANT IRS TO FIGURE YOUR TAX, PLEASE STOP HERE AND SIGN BELOW.			
b	Total Federal income tax withheld (*If line 7 is more than $22,900, see page 12 of Instructions*) **12b** 1179 86			
c	Earned income credit (*from page 2 of Instructions*) . . . . **12c** O			
13	Total (*add lines 12a, b, and c*)	13		

4.

7	Wages, salaries, tips, etc. *(Attach Forms W–2. If you do not have a W–2, see page 10 of Instructions)*	**7**	16,814 91
8	Interest income *(See pages 4 and 10 of Instructions)*	**8**	0
9a	Dividends ___141 00___ (See pages 4 and 10 of Instructions) 9b Exclusion ___112 00___ Subtract line 9b from 9a	**9c**	
10a	Unemployment compensation. Total amount received ___0___		
b	Taxable part, if any, from worksheet on page 11 of Instructions	**10b**	0
11	Adjusted gross income *(add lines 7, 8, 9c, and 10b). If under $10,000, see page 2 of Instructions on "Earned Income Credit"*	**11**	

12a	Credit for contributions to candidates for public office. (See page 11 of Instructions)	**12a**	16 00

IF YOU WANT IRS TO FIGURE YOUR TAX, PLEASE STOP HERE AND SIGN BELOW.

b	Total Federal income tax withheld *(If line 7 is more than $22,900, see page 12 of Instructions)*	**12b**	4203 50
c	Earned income credit *(from page 2 of Instructions)*	**12c**	0
13	Total *(add lines 12a, b, and c)*	**13**	

Please Attach Copy B of Forms W–2

> **SKILL:** Using tax tables when filing a 1040A tax return.

To continue completing Al Q. Taxpayer's 1040A form, you must be able to read an *income tax table.*

If Form 1040A, line 11, is—		And the total number of exemptions claimed on line 6 is-		
Over	But not over	**1**	**2**	**3**
		Your tax is—		
8,500	8,550	887	697	517
8,550	8,600	896	706	526
8,600	8,650	906	716	535
8,650	8,700	915	725	544
8,700	8,750	925	735	553
8,750	8,800	934	744	562
8,800	8,850	944	754	571
8,850	8,900	953	763	580
8,900	8,950	963	773	589
8,950	9,000	972	782	598
9,000	9,050	982	792	607
9,050	9,100	991	801	616
9,100	9,150	1,001	811	625
9,150	9,200	1,010	820	634
9,200	9,250	1,020	830	643
9,250	9,300	1,029	839	652
9,300	9,350	1,039	849	661
9,350	9,400	1,048	858	670
9,400	9,450	1,058	868	679
9,450	9,500	1,067	877	688
9,500	9,550	1,077	887	697
9,550	9,600	1,088	896	706
9,600	9,650	1,098	906	716
9,650	9,700	1,109	915	725

STEP 1:
    a. Read down the left hand column of the tax table shown above until you come to the numbers that $8,875 comes between. (DO THIS NOW.)
    b. Imagine a line that goes under these numbers and continues all the way across the tax table.

STEP 2:
    a. At the top of this tax table, find the number of exemptions being claimed. In this case, it is 2.
    b. Imagine another line down through the column for 2 exemptions.
    c. These two imaginary lines going down and across the tax table will meet at a number.
    d. This number is the amount of tax on an adjusted gross income of $8,875 with 2 exemptions.
    e. It will be different if fewer or more exemptions are claimed.

Use the tax table on page 238 to find the tax for these two incomes:

(a) $9,045.00—claiming 3 exemptions.

(b) $9,587 —claiming 2 exemptions.

Anja also explains to Miro and Ranzo that there are four tax tables, depending on a person's *filing status:* (1) single; (2) married, filing joint return; (3) married, filing separate return; and (4) head of household. When filling out Form 1040A, you must use the tax table for your filing status.

Use the tax tables for Form 1040A provided by your teacher to find the tax for each of the following situations:

Filing Status	Adjusted Gross Income	Exemptions
√ 1. Single	$12,642.53	2
√ 2. Married Filing Joint Return	18,943.63	3
3. Married Filing Separate Returns	19,552.78	2
4. Married Filing Joint Return	8,457.31	4
5. Head of Household	15,636.28	3
6. Single	7,482.50	1
7. Married Filing Joint Return	10,681.37	2

Tax Time!

Filing Status	Adjusted Gross Income	Exemptions
8. Single	4,863.81	1
9. Married Filing Separate Returns	12,638.54	2
10. Single	17,463.81	1

Now go back to the 1040A form that your teacher gave you to fill out for Al Q. Taxpayer. You are ready to complete items 14 and 15 on the form. Assume that Al received no advance earned income credit payments, so item 14b will be 0. *Make sure you use the proper tax table for Al's filing status.* (The information box on page 236 contains enough details for you to decide what his filing status is.)

When you have completed items 14 and 15 on the 1040A form, show the form to your teacher.

SKILL: Figuring if you will get a refund or owe more money when filing a 1040A tax return.

Complete the 1040A form for Al Q. Taxpayer by following the directions for Items 16 or 17. (DO THIS NOW.)

You prepared Mr. Al Q. Taxpayer's income tax return. What will you tell him?

a. "Congratulations, you get a refund of _____!"

b. "I'm sorry, Mr. Taxpayer, but you owe _____ more for income tax."

Practice figuring the amount to be *refunded* or the amount of *balance due* in the following tax returns:

√ 1.

Attach Payment Here

13 Total *(add lines 12a, b, and c)*	13	873 51

14a Tax on the amount on line 11. *(See Instructions for line 14a on page 12; then find your tax in the Tax Tables on pages 15–26.)* 14a 1686 52

b Advance earned income credit payments received *(from Form W–2)*   14b 0

15 Total *(add lines 14a and 14b)* 15 1686 52

16 If line 13 is larger than line 15, enter amount to be **REFUNDED TO YOU** . . . . . . ▶   16

17 If line 15 is larger than line 13, enter **BALANCE DUE.** Attach check or money order for full amount payable to "Internal Revenue Service." Write your social security number on check or money order . ▶   17

√ 2.

Attach Payment Here

13 Total *(add lines 12a, b, and c)* 13 2563 89

14a Tax on the amount on line 11. *(See Instructions for line 14a on page 12; then find your tax in the Tax Tables on pages 15–26.)* 14a 1964 38

b Advance earned income credit payments received *(from Form W–2)* 14b 0

15 Total *(add lines 14a and 14b)* 15 1964 38

16 If line 13 is larger than line 15, enter amount to be **REFUNDED TO YOU** . . . . . . ▶   16

17 If line 15 is larger than line 13, enter **BALANCE DUE.** Attach check or money order for full amount payable to "Internal Revenue Service." Write your social security number on check or money order . ▶   17

3.

Attach Payment Here

13 Total *(add lines 12a, b, and c)* 13 658 35

14a Tax on the amount on line 11. *(See Instructions for line 14a on page 12; then find your tax in the Tax Tables on pages 15–26.)* 14a 597 82

b Advance earned income credit payments received *(from Form W–2)* 14b

15 Total *(add lines 14a and 14b)* 15 597 82

16 If line 13 is larger than line 15, enter amount to be **REFUNDED TO YOU** . . . . . . ▶   16

17 If line 15 is larger than line 13, enter **BALANCE DUE.** Attach check or money order for full amount payable to "Internal Revenue Service." Write your social security number on check or money order . ▶   17

4.

Attach Payment Here

13 Total *(add lines 12a, b, and c)* 13 384 18

14a Tax on the amount on line 11. *(See Instructions for line 14a on page 12; then find your tax in the Tax Tables on pages 15–26.)* 14a 659 00

b Advance earned income credit payments received *(from Form W–2)* 14b 0

15 Total *(add lines 14a and 14b)* 15 659 00

16 If line 13 is larger than line 15, enter amount to be **REFUNDED TO YOU** . . . . . . ▶   16

17 If line 15 is larger than line 13, enter **BALANCE DUE.** Attach check or money order for full amount payable to "Internal Revenue Service." Write your social security number on check or money order . ▶   17

5.

Attach Payment Here

13 Total *(add lines 12a, b, and c)* 13 1021 53

14a Tax on the amount on line 11. *(See Instructions for line 14a on page 12; then find your tax in the Tax Tables on pages 15–26.)* 14a 1765 99

b Advance earned income credit payments received *(from Form W–2)* 14b 0

15 Total *(add lines 14a and 14b)* 15 1765 99

16 If line 13 is larger than line 15, enter amount to be **REFUNDED TO YOU** . . . . . . ▶   16

17 If line 15 is larger than line 13, enter **BALANCE DUE.** Attach check or money order for full amount payable to "Internal Revenue Service." Write your social security number on check or money order . ▶   17

6.

13	Total *(add lines 12a, b, and c)*			**13**	348 | 91
14a	Tax on the amount on line 11. *(See Instructions for line 14a on page 12; then find your tax in the Tax Tables on pages 15–26.)*	**14a**	217 | 67		
b	Advance earned income credit payments received *(from Form W–2)*	**14b**	0		
15	Total *(add lines 14a and 14b)*.			**15**	217 | 67
16	If line 13 is larger than line 15, enter amount to be **REFUNDED TO YOU** . . . . ▶			**16**	
17	If line 15 is larger than line 13, enter **BALANCE DUE.** Attach check or money order for full amount payable to "Internal Revenue Service." Write your social security number on check or money order . ▶			**17**	

Attach Payment Here

7.

13	Total *(add lines 12a, b, and c)*			**13**	4281 | 50
14a	Tax on the amount on line 11. *(See Instructions for line 14a on page 12; then find your tax in the Tax Tables on pages 15–26.)*	**14a**	3182 | 58		
b	Advance earned income credit payments received *(from Form W–2)*	**14b**	0		
15	Total *(add lines 14a and 14b)*.			**15**	3182 | 58
16	If line 13 is larger than line 15, enter amount to be **REFUNDED TO YOU** . . . . ▶			**16**	
17	If line 15 is larger than line 13, enter **BALANCE DUE.** Attach check or money order for full amount payable to "Internal Revenue Service." Write your social security number on check or money order . ▶			**17**	

Attach Payment Here

8.

13	Total *(add lines 12a, b, and c)*			**13**	3500 | 07
14a	Tax on the amount on line 11. *(See Instructions for line 14a on page 12; then find your tax in the Tax Tables on pages 15–26.)*	**14a**	4116 | 29		
b	Advance earned income credit payments received *(from Form W–2)*	**14b**	0		
15	Total *(add lines 14a and 14b)*.			**15**	4116 | 29
16	If line 13 is larger than line 15, enter amount to be **REFUNDED TO YOU** . . . . ▶			**16**	
17	If line 15 is larger than line 13, enter **BALANCE DUE.** Attach check or money order for full amount payable to "Internal Revenue Service." Write your social security number on check or money order . ▶			**17**	

Attach Payment Here

SKILL: Using a gasoline tax rate table when itemizing deductions.

1. The tax rate on gasoline is different from state to state.
2. A *State Gasoline Tax Rate Table* helps you figure how much you've spent on gasoline tax in your state.

Look at the list of states in the top section of the table below. The list shows what the tax is in each state on every gallon of gas.

STATE GASOLINE TAX RATE TABLE

Alabama 7¢	Georgia 7.5¢	Massachusetts 8.5¢	New York 8¢	South Dakota 8¢
Alaska 8¢	Hawaii 8.5¢	Michigan 9¢	North Carolina 9¢	Tennessee 7¢
Arizona 8¢	Idaho 9.5¢	Minnesota 9¢	North Dakota 8¢	Texas 5¢
Arkansas 8.5¢	Illinois 7.5¢	Mississippi 9¢	Ohio 7¢	Utah 9¢
California 7¢	Indiana 8¢	Missouri 7¢	Oklahoma 6.58¢	Vermont 9¢
Colorado 7¢	Iowa 8.5¢	Montana 8¢	(use deduction	Virginia 9¢
Connecticut 11¢	Kansas 8¢	Nebraska 9.5¢	for 6.5¢)	Washington 11¢
Delaware 9¢	Kentucky 9¢	Nevada 6¢	Oregon 7¢	West Virginia 10.5¢
District of	Louisiana 8¢	New Hampshire 10¢	Pennsylvania 9¢	Wisconsin 7¢
Columbia 10¢	Maine 9¢	New Jersey 8¢	Rhode Island 10¢	Wyoming 8¢
Florida 8¢	Maryland 9¢	New Mexico 7¢	South Carolina 9¢	

Miles Driven	Tax Rate Per Gallon of Gasoline											
	5¢	6¢	6.5¢	7¢	7.5¢	8¢	8.5¢	9¢	9.5¢	10¢	10.5¢	11¢
Under 3,000	$ 8	$10	$11	$12	$12	$13	$14	$15	$16	$17	$17	$18
3,000 under 4,000	14	17	19	20	22	23	25	26	27	29	30	32
4,000 under 5,000	19	22	24	26	28	30	32	33	35	37	39	41
5,000 under 6,000	23	27	30	32	34	36	39	41	43	46	48	50
6,000 under 7,000	27	32	35	38	40	43	46	48	51	54	56	59
7,000 under 8,000	31	37	40	43	47	50	53	56	59	62	65	68
8,000 under 9,000	35	42	46	49	53	56	60	63	67	70	74	77
9,000 under 10,000	39	47	51	55	59	63	67	71	75	79	82	86
10,000 under 11,000	43	52	56	61	65	69	74	78	82	87	91	93
11,000 under 12,000	48	57	62	67	71	76	81	86	90	95	100	105
12,000 under 13,000	52	62	67	72	77	83	88	93	98	103	108	114
13,000 under 14,000	56	67	73	78	84	89	95	100	106	112	117	123
14,000 under 15,000	60	72	78	84	90	96	102	108	114	120	126	132
15,000 under 16,000	64	77	83	90	96	102	109	115	122	128	135	141
16,000 under 17,000	68	82	89	95	102	109	116	123	130	135	143	150
17,000 under 18,000	72	87	94	101	108	116	123	130	137	145	152	159
18,000 under 19,000	76	92	99	107	115	122	130	138	145	153	161	168
19,000 under 20,000	81	97	105	113	121	129	137	145	153	161	169	177
20,000*	83	99	107	116	124	132	141	149	157	165	174	182

*For over 20,000 miles, use table amounts for total miles driven. For example, for 25,000 miles, add the deduction for 5,000 to the deduction for 20,000 miles.

1. Look down the left side of the table to find the number of miles you've driven during the year.

2. Then, read across the table until you come to the number in the TAX RATE column that is correct for the state given.

   Example: Nevada   - go to 6¢ column
                   Maine   - go to 9¢ column
                   Massachusetts - go to 8.5¢ column

Tax Time!

For each problem below, find the amount you could list as a deduction. Use State Gasoline Tax Rate Table shown on page 245.

√ 1. Miles driven: 14,683
   State: Nebraska

√ 2. Miles driven: 2,306
   State: Lousiana

3. Miles driven: 14,010
   State: Kentucky

4. Miles driven: 4,847
   State: Michigan

5. Miles driven: 17,453
   State: Nevada

6. Miles driven: 13,886
   State: New York

7. Miles driven: 18,416
   State: Montana

8. Miles driven: 9,751
   State: Illinois

9. Miles driven: 16,200
   State: Maine

10. Miles driven: 14,285
    State: Florida

11. Miles Driven: 19,561
    State: Rhode Island

12. Miles Driven: 17,500
    State: Hawaii

Chapter 9
Self-Test

For items 1-4, use the sales tax table below to find the tax on each purchase. (See pages 224-231.)

6% SALES TAX TABLE

Sale Amount	Tax	Sale Amount	Tax	Sale Amount	Tax	Sale Amount	Tax
$ .00— .10	None	$2.35—2.50	.15	$5.11—5.17	.31	$7.68— 7.84	.47
.11— .17	.01	2.51—2.67	.16	5.18—5.34	.32	7.85— 8.10	.48
.18— .34	.02	2.68—2.84	.17	5.35—5.50	.33	8.11— 8.17	.49
.35— .50	.03	2.85—3.10	.18	5.51—5.67	.34	8.18— 8.34	.50
.51— .67	.04	3.11—3.17	.19	5.68—5.84	.35	8.35— 8.50	.51
.68— .84	.05	3.18—3.34	.20	5.85—6.10	.36	8.51— 8.67	.52
.85—1.10	.06	3.35—3.50	.21	6.11—6.17	.37	8.68— 8.84	.53
1.11—1.17	.07	3.51—3.67	.22	6.18—6.34	.38	8.85— 9.10	.54
1.18—1.34	.08	3.68—3.84	.23	6.35—6.50	.39	9.11— 9.17	.55
1.35—1.50	.09	3.85—4.10	.24	6.51—6.67	.40	9.18— 9.34	.56
1.51—1.67	.10	4.11—4.17	.25	6.68—6.84	.41	9.35— 9.50	.57
1.68—1.84	.11	4.18—4.34	.26	6.85—7.10	.42	9.51— 9.67	.58
1.85—2.10	.12	4.35—4.50	.27	7.11—7.17	.43	9.68— 9.84	.59
2.11—2.17	.13	4.51—4.67	.28	7.18—7.34	.44	9.85—10.00	.60
2.18—2.34	.14	4.68—4.84	.29	7.35—7.50	.45		
		4.85—5.10	.30	7.51—7.67	.46		

1. Beans: 53¢
   Sales tax?

2. Art supplies: $9.66
   Sales tax?

3. Roller skates: $24.92
   Sales tax?

4. Luggage: $120.16
   Sales tax?

Use the form below to answer items 5-7. (See pages 232-238.)

7	Wages, salaries, tips, etc. (*Attach Forms W-2. If you do not have a W-2, see page 10 of Instructions*)	7	12,467 78
8	Interest income (*See pages 4 and 10 of Instructions*)	8	63 42
9a	Dividends 179 25 (*See pages 4 and 10 of Instructions*) 9b Exclusion 100 00 Subtract line 9b from 9a	9c	
10a	Unemployment compensation. Total amount received 0		
b	Taxable part, if any, from worksheet on page 11 of Instructions	10b	0
11	Adjusted gross income (*add lines 7, 8, 9c, and 10b*). If under $10,000, see page 2 of Instructions on "Earned Income Credit"	11	
12a	Credit for contributions to candidates for public office. (*See page 11 of Instructions*) 12a 0		

IF YOU WANT IRS TO FIGURE YOUR TAX, PLEASE STOP HERE AND SIGN BELOW.

b	Total Federal income tax withheld (*If line 7 is more than $22,900, see page 12 of Instructions*) 12b 2135 13		
c	Earned income credit (*from page 2 of Instructions*) 12c 0		
13	Total (*add lines 12a, b, and c*)	13	

5. What figure should be in slot 9c?

6. What figure should be in slot 11?

7. What figure should be in slot 13?

Use the form below to answer items 8 and 9. (See pages 232-238.)

7	Wages, salaries, tips, etc. (*Attach Forms W-2. If you do not have a W-2, see page 10 of Instructions*)	7	16,259 72
8	Interest income (*See pages 4 and 10 of Instructions*)	8	403 04
9a	Dividends 0 (*See pages 4 and 10 of Instructions*) 9b Exclusion 0 Subtract line 9b from 9a	9c	
10a	Unemployment compensation. Total amount received 0		
b	Taxable part, if any, from worksheet on page 11 of Instructions	10b	0
11	Adjusted gross income (*add lines 7, 8, 9c, and 10b*). If under $10,000, see page 2 of Instructions on "Earned Income Credit"	11	
12a	Credit for contributions to candidates for public office. (*See page 11 of Instructions*) 12a 25 00		

IF YOU WANT IRS TO FIGURE YOUR TAX, PLEASE STOP HERE AND SIGN BELOW.

b	Total Federal income tax withheld (*If line 7 is more than $22,900, see page 12 of Instructions*) 12b 1996 40		
c	Earned income credit (*from page 2 of Instructions*) 12c 0		
13	Total (*add lines 12a, b, and c*)	13	

8. What figure should be in slot 11?

9. What figure should be in slot 13?

For items 10-15, use the tax table to find the tax for each situation. (See pages 238-241.)

If Form 1040A, line 11, is—		And the total number of exemptions claimed on line 6 is—							
Over	But not over	1	2	3	4	5	6	7	8
		Your tax is—							
11,500	11,550	1,428	1,208	995	815	635	474	314	172
11,550	11,600	1,439	1,219	1,004	824	644	482	322	179
11,600	11,650	1,450	1,230	1,013	833	653	490	330	186
11,650	11,700	1,461	1,241	1,022	842	662	498	338	193
11,700	11,750	1,472	1,252	1,032	851	671	506	346	200
11,750	11,800	1,483	1,263	1,043	860	680	514	354	207
11,800	11,850	1,494	1,274	1,054	869	689	522	362	214
11,850	11,900	1,505	1,285	1,065	878	698	530	370	221
11,900	11,950	1,516	1,296	1,076	887	707	538	378	228
11,950	12,000	1,527	1,307	1,087	896	716	546	386	235
12,000	12,050	1,538	1,318	1,098	905	725	554	394	242
12,050	12,100	1,549	1,329	1,109	914	734	562	402	249
12,100	12,150	1,560	1,340	1,120	923	743	570	410	256
12,150	12,200	1,571	1,351	1,131	932	752	578	418	263
12,200	12,250	1,582	1,362	1,142	941	761	586	426	270
12,250	12,300	1,593	1,373	1,153	950	770	594	434	277
12,300	12,350	1,604	1,384	1,164	959	779	602	442	284
12,350	12,400	1,615	1,395	1,175	968	788	610	450	291
12,400	12,450	1,626	1,406	1,186	977	797	618	458	298
12,450	12,500	1,637	1,417	1,197	986	806	626	466	306
12,500	12,550	1,648	1,428	1,208	995	815	635	474	314
12,550	12,600	1,659	1,439	1,219	1,004	824	644	482	322
12,600	12,650	1,670	1,450	1,230	1,013	833	653	490	330
12,650	12,700	1,681	1,461	1,241	1,022	842	662	498	338
12,700	12,750	1,692	1,472	1,252	1,032	851	671	506	346
12,750	12,800	1,703	1,483	1,263	1,043	860	680	514	354
12,800	12,850	1,714	1,494	1,274	1,054	869	689	522	362
12,850	12,900	1,726	1,505	1,285	1,065	878	698	530	370
12,900	12,950	1,738	1,516	1,296	1,076	887	707	538	378
12,950	13,000	1,750	1,527	1,307	1,087	896	716	546	386
13,000	13,050	1,762	1,538	1,318	1,098	905	725	554	394
13,050	13,100	1,774	1,549	1,329	1,109	914	734	562	402
13,100	13,150	1,786	1,560	1,340	1,120	923	743	570	410
13,150	13,200	1,798	1,571	1,351	1,131	932	752	578	418
13,200	13,250	1,810	1,582	1,362	1,142	941	761	586	426
13,250	13,300	1,822	1,593	1,373	1,153	950	770	594	434
13,300	13,350	1,834	1,604	1,384	1,164	959	779	602	442
13,350	13,400	1,846	1,615	1,395	1,175	968	788	610	4
13,400	13,450		626		186	977		618	

10. Adjusted Gross Income:
$12,278.16
Exemptions:3

11. Adjusted Gross Income:
$11,775.00
Exemptions: 5

12. Adjusted Gross Income:
$13,118.33
Exemptions: 4

13. Adjusted Gross Income:
$11,985.21
Exemptions: 6

14. Adjusted Gross Income:
$12,400.62
Exemptions: 7

15. Adjusted Gross Income:
$13,139.19
Exemptions: 2

Use the form below to answer items 16 and 17. (See pages 241-243.)

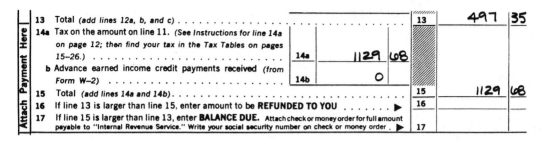

16. What figure, if any, should be in slot 16?

17. What figure, if any, should be in slot 17?

Use the form below to answer items 18 and 19. (See pages 241-243.)

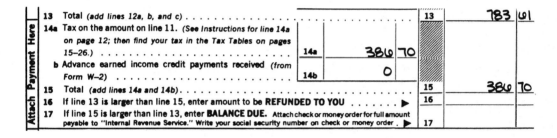

18. What figure, if any, should be in slot 16?

19. What figure, if any, should be in slot 17?

Use the form below to answer items 20 and 21. (See pages 241-243.)

13 Total (add lines 12a, b, and c) . . . . | 13 | 458 |34
14a Tax on the amount on line 11. (See Instructions for line 14a
    on page 12; then find your tax in the Tax Tables on pages
    15–26.) . . . . | 14a | 458 34 |
   b Advance earned income credit payments received (from
    Form W–2) . . . . | 14b | O |
15 Total (add lines 14a and 14b). . . . . | 15 | 458 |34
16 If line 13 is larger than line 15, enter amount to be REFUNDED TO YOU . . . . . . ▶ | 16 |
17 If line 15 is larger than line 13, enter BALANCE DUE. Attach check or money order for full amount
    payable to "Internal Revenue Service." Write your social security number on check or money order . ▶ | 17 |

20. What figure, if any, should be in slot 16?

21. What figure, if any, should be in slot 17?

Tax Time!

Use the Gasoline Tax Rate Table below to answer items 22-26. (See pages 243-247.)

STATE GASOLINE TAX RATE TABLE

Alabama 7¢	Georgia 7.5¢	Massachusetts 8.5¢	New York 8¢	South Dakota 8¢
Alaska 8¢	Hawaii 8.5¢	Michigan 9¢	North Carolina 9¢	Tennessee 7¢
Arizona 8¢	Idaho 9.5¢	Minnesota 9¢	North Dakota 8¢	Texas 5¢
Arkansas 8.5¢	Illinois 7.5¢	Mississippi 9¢	Ohio 7¢	Utah 9¢
California 7¢	Indiana 8¢	Missouri 7¢	Oklahoma 6.58¢	Vermont 9¢
Colorado 7¢	Iowa 8.5¢	Montana 8¢	(use deduction	Virginia 9¢
Connecticut 11¢	Kansas 8¢	Nebraska 9.5¢	for 6.5¢)	Washington 11¢
Delaware 9¢	Kentucky 9¢	Nevada 6¢	Oregon 7¢	West Virginia 10.5¢
District of	Louisiana 8¢	New Hampshire 10¢	Pennsylvania 9¢	Wisconsin 7¢
Columbia 10¢	Maine 9¢	New Jersey 8¢	Rhode Island 10¢	Wyoming 8¢
Florida 8¢	Maryland 9¢	New Mexico 7¢	South Carolina 9¢	

Miles Driven	Tax Rate Per Gallon of Gasoline											
	5¢	6¢	6.5¢	7¢	7.5¢	8¢	8.5¢	9¢	9.5¢	10¢	10.5¢	11¢
Under 3,000	$ 8	$10	$11	$12	$12	$13	$14	$15	$16	$17	$17	$18
3,000 under 4,000	14	17	19	20	22	23	25	26	27	29	30	32
4,000 under 5,000	19	22	24	26	28	30	32	33	35	37	39	41
5,000 under 6,000	23	27	30	32	34	36	39	41	43	46	48	50
6,000 under 7,000	27	32	35	38	40	43	46	48	51	54	56	59
7,000 under 8,000	31	37	40	43	47	50	53	56	59	62	65	68
8,000 under 9,000	35	42	46	49	53	56	60	63	67	70	74	77
9,000 under 10,000	39	47	51	55	59	63	67	71	75	79	82	86
10,000 under 11,000	43	52	56	61	65	69	74	78	82	87	91	93
11,000 under 12,000	48	57	62	67	71	76	81	86	90	95	100	105
12,000 under 13,000	52	62	67	72	77	83	88	93	98	103	108	114
13,000 under 14,000	56	67	73	78	84	89	95	100	106	112	117	123
14,000 under 15,000	60	72	78	84	90	96	102	108	114	120	126	132
15,000 under 16,000	64	77	83	90	96	102	109	115	122	128	135	141
16,000 under 17,000	68	82	89	95	102	109	116	123	130	135	143	150
17,000 under 18,000	72	87	94	101	108	116	123	130	137	145	152	159
18,000 under 19,000	76	92	99	107	115	122	130	138	145	153	161	168
19,000 under 20,000	81	97	105	113	121	129	137	145	153	161	169	177
20,000*	83	99	107	116	124	132	141	149	157	165	174	182

*For over 20,000 miles, use table amounts for total miles driven. For example, for 25,000 miles, add the deduction for 5,000 to the deduction for 20,000 miles.

What amount could be listed as a deduction in each of the following situations?

22. Miles driven: 9,462
    State: New Hampshire

23. Miles driven: 19,462
    State: Illinois

24. Miles driven: 21,000
    State: Texas

25. Miles driven: 9,541
    State: Mississippi

26. Miles driven: 13,993
    State: Washington

CHAPTER

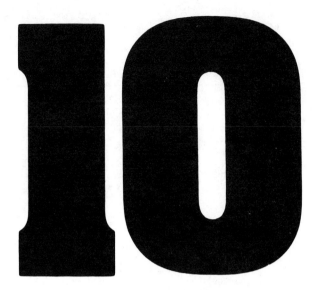

BUYING INSURANCE

USING BASIC MATH SKILLS TO SOLVE PROBLEMS RELATED TO INSURANCE.

KEY WORDS:

1. **Automobile Insurance:** protects you against the money costs of automobile accidents.

2. **Automobile Liability Insurance:** protects the other person, if you hit him or damage his property in an auto accident.

3. **Collision Insurance:** this pays to replace your car if you damage it.

4. **Comprehensive Insurance:** will pay to repair your car if it is damaged or destroyed in an accident that doesn't involve another car. It will also replace your car if it is stolen.

5. **Compulsory Automobile Insurance:** a term which means the same as automobile liability insurance.

6. **Deductible:** when you agree to pay for *some* of the costs yourself. If you have ''$50 deductible'' insurance, you pay the *first* $50 of the bill. Likewise, if you have ''$100 deductible'' insurance, you pay the first $100.

7. **Disability Insurance:** paid for through your Social Security deductions. It insures you a small monthly income if you lose your job because of illness or injury.

8. **Health Insurance:** protects you against the money costs of being sick or injured.

9. **Hospital Health Insurance:** pays for medicines and services you receive while you are staying in a hospital. It also pays for some or all of the costs for visiting the emergency room of a hospital.

10. **Hospitalization:** a term which means the same as hospital health insurance.

11. **Insurance Policy:** an agreement between you and an insurance company that it will provide certain amounts of money when specific situations require it.

12. **Life Insurance:** provides financial help to your family if you die from sickness or injury.

13. **Medical Payments Insurance:** pays for medical and hospital costs for you and your passengers if your car is involved in a serious accident.

14. **Nonhospital Health Insurance:** pays for some or all of your doctor's bills. It *may* also pay for some medicines, tests, and exams as long as you are *not* actually *staying* in a hospital.

15. **Road Service/Towing Insurance:** pays for services you may need if your car breaks down on the road.

16. **Term Life Insurance:** provides financial help to your family if you die within a specific period of time from illness or injury.

17. **Unemployment Insurance:** an insurance paid for by your employer. It insures you will receive a small income if you should lose your job through no fault of your own.

18. **Uninsured Motorist Insurance:** makes sure you can collect money even though a driver who injures you or your property may *not* be covered by liability insurance.

SKILL: Recognizing the availability of different kinds of insurance.

Accidents are always going to cost you something, but if you have the right kinds of *insurance*, they may not cost you a lot of money. Insurance protects you against the money costs of accidents. It can also protect you against the money costs of losing things that are valuable.

Persons who work for a living usually have some kinds of insurance already.

If you lose your job through no fault of your own, you can collect **Unemployment Insurance.** This gives you a small weekly income while you look for another job. Your employer pays for this insurance.

If you lose your job because of sickness or injury, you can collect **Disability Insurance.** This gives you a small monthly income. You help pay for this insurance with your Social Security (F.I.C.A.) deductions from your paychecks.

Buying Insurance

Insurance to cover "The Other Guy" if you hit him or damage his property in an auto accident.

Insurance to pay hospital and doctor bills when you are sick or injured in an automobile accident.

Insurance to help your family if you die from sickness or injury.

No matter what kind of insurance protection you buy, what you are buying is an *insurance policy.* An insurance policy is an agreement between you and an insurance company that it will provide certain amounts of money when specific situations require it.

1. The *amounts* of money the policy will provide.

2. The *kinds* of situations the policy covers.

3. The *amount* of money *you pay* for the policy.

. . . . . $25,000 . . . .
. . . .
. . . .
$5,000 . . . .
. . . .
. . . .
. . . .
. . . . $3,000 . . . .
. . . .

Accidental Death . . . .
. . . .
Loss of Property . . . .
. . . .
. . . .
Loss of Rights . . . .
. . . .
. . . .
. . . .

. . . .
. . . .
. . . .
. . . .
I agree to pay $15.00 per month (three years, $540).
. . . .
. . . .

Remember, also, the cheapest policy isn't always the best. Make sure you buy your insurance from a company you can trust.

Buying insurance always involves making choices. What *kinds* of insurance you buy depends on what kinds of protection you think you need. How much insurance you buy depends on how much money you can afford to spend for it.

If you own a car, you will probably have to buy *automobile liability insurance.* It is a law in many states that car owners must buy this kind of insurance. This insurance is also sometimes called *compulsory auto insurance.*

In many states, the minimum amounts of liability insurance you have to buy are set by law. The amounts you buy are described by three numbers.

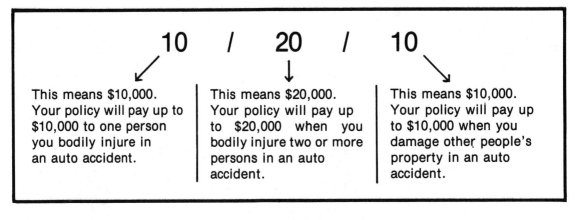

10 / 20 / 10

This means $10,000. Your policy will pay up to $10,000 to one person you bodily injure in an auto accident.

This means $20,000. Your policy will pay up to $20,000 when you bodily injure two or more persons in an auto accident.

This means $10,000. Your policy will pay up to $10,000 when you damage other people's property in an auto accident.

In some states, the minimum you have to buy is very low, as low as "5/10/1."

5 / 10 / 1

$5,000. Your policy will pay up to $5,000 to one person you bodily injure in an auto accident.

$10,000. Your policy will pay up to $10,000 when you bodily injure two or more persons in an auto accident.

$1,000. Your policy will pay up to $1,000 when you damage other people's property in an auto accident.

IMPORTANT: A serious auto accident could cost *much more* than the amounts paid by this insurance policy. For this reason, you should buy as much liability insurance as you can reasonably afford. Many people buy as much as their insurance company policies will allow—as high as "50/100/25."

Most auto liability insurance policies last only six months. You have to *renew* your policy to keep protected. This simply means that you have to "buy" your policy twice a year to be protected for a whole year. To find the yearly cost, just multiply the cost of the six month policy times 2.

A driver's age makes a big difference in the cost of liability insurance. The younger you are, the more you pay. Here is a list of the different kinds of liability protection a typical insurance sells to young drivers.

ACE INSURANCE COMPANY
Auto Liability Insurance
6 Month Policy

5/10/5	$125.75	20/40/20	$137.36
10/20/10	$131.16	25/50/10	$137.98
15/30/10	$132.28	25/50/25	$138.40
15/30/15	$133.25	50/100/25	$139.75
20/40/10	$136.74	50/100/50	$140.98

THE COSTS FOR EACH AMOUNT OF PROTECTION IS FOR 6 MONTHS. REMEMBER, TO FIND THE TOTAL **YEARLY** COST, MULTIPLY THE AMOUNT TIMES 2.

SAMPLE:

Glenn Shirrell   25/50/10

$137.98   (COST FOR 6 MONTHS

  x   2

$275.96   (COST PER YEAR)

Use the insurance price list above to determine the total yearly cost of liability insurance for each buyer in the problems below.

√1. Howard Lemon, 25/50/25

√2. Carmen Crash, 5/10/5

3. Jill Junk, 50/100/50

4. Jerry Cracksupalot, 10/20/10

5. Manuel Dent, 15/30/15

6. Joyce Brakes, 50/100/25

7. Ann X. Ident, 25/50/10

8. Carol Collision, 20/40/20

9. Alicia Fenderbender, 15/30/10

10. Javier Bumper, 20/40/10

Use the following insurance price list to determine the total *yearly* cost of auto liability insurance for different drivers. (The list of each kind of liability insurance is for six months.)

SAMPLE:

Bill Dodge, 15/30/15

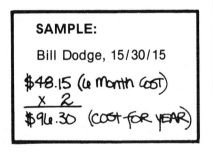

IDEAL INSURANCE COMPANY
Automobile Liability Insurance
6 Month Policy

5/10/5 . . . . $45.65	20/40/20 . . . . . $51.63
10/20/10 . . . . . $46.78	25/50/10 . . . . . $54.94
15/30/10 . . . . . $47.93	25/50/25 . . . . . $55.75
15/30/15 . . . . . $48.15	50/100/25 . . . . $56.23
20/40/10 . . . . . $50.65	50/100/50 . . . . $58.18

1. Carol Datsun, 25/50/25

2. Doug Pacer, 5/10/5

3. John Rabbit, 50/100/25

4. Wayne Kombi, 15/30/10

5. Kay Pontiac, 50/100/50

6. Len Oldsmobile, 20/40/20

7. Chris Chevy, 10/20/10

8. Eleanor Ford, 25/50/10

9. Jan Audi, 20/40/10

Buying Insurance

The more valuable your car is, the more important it is to buy these two kinds of insurance. But if your car is not worth very much, it probably won't pay you to buy the comprehensive and collision insurance. You may pay more for the insurance than you'd get back to repair or replace your car.

UNINSURED MOTORIST INSURANCE

This makes sure you can collect money even though a driver who injures you or your property may *not* be covered by liability insurance.

MEDICAL PAYMENTS INSURANCE

This pays for medical and hospital costs for you and your passengers if your car becomes involved in a serious accident.

ROAD SERVICE/TOWING INSURANCE

This helps to pay for services you might need if your car breaks down on the road.

SAMPLE:

BETTER-NOT-BUMP INSURANCE COMPANY
Policy

Liability (50/100/50) .... $ 36.40
Comprehensive 25.90
$25 Deductible Collision 53.40
Uninsured Motorist 12.98
Road Service/Towing 1.25

TOTAL COST.... $129.93

STEP 1: Add the costs

$ 36.40
25.90
53.40
12.98
1.25
_____
$ 129.93

Find the total costs of the following auto insurance policies.

√ 1.

Liability (50/100/50)	$ 40.62
Comprehensive	27.83
Medical Payments	17.40
Uninsured Motorist	16.30
TOTAL . . . . . $	

√ 2.

Liability (50/100/50)	$ 38.17
$100 Deductible Collision	25.80
Uninsured Motorist	16.42
Medical Payments	18.95
Road Service/Towing	2.50
TOTAL . . . . . $	

3.

Liability (60/100/25)	$ 31.90
Comprehensive	26.10
Medical Payments	14.30
TOTAL . . . . . $	

4.

Liability (50/100/50)	$ 30.04
Comprehensive	15.00
$50 Deductible Collision	30.72
Road Service/Towing	1.56
TOTAL . . . . . $	

5.

Liability (50/100/25)	$ 31.43
Comprehensive	26.75
$50 Deductible Collision	38.17
Uninsured Motorist	18.62
Medical Payments	17.98
Road Service/Towing	1.25
TOTAL . . . . . $	

6.

Liability (50/100/10)	$ 29.42
Comprehensive	21.38
Medical Payments	15.30
TOTAL . . . . . $	

7.

Liability (50/100/25)	$ 32.15
$100 Deductible Collision	29.17
Uninsured Motorist	17.19
Road Service/Towing	1.65
TOTAL . . . . . $	

8.

Liability (50/100/50)	$ 33.28
Comprehensive	27.43
$50 Deductible Collision	41.16
Medical Payments	16.51
Uninsured Motorist	18.42
Road Service/Towing	1.50
TOTAL . . . . . $	

9.

Liability (50/100/15) . . . . $	31.16
Comprehensive	24.92
Road Service/Towing	2.00
TOTAL . . . . . $	

10.

Liability (50/100/50) . . . . $	34.98
Comprehensive	27.63
$100 Deductible Collision	27.19
Medical Payments	12.43
Uninsured Motorist	17.91
TOTAL . . . . . $	

For more practice in finding the total cost of automobile insurance, work the following problems.

1.

Liability (50/100/50) . . . . $	45.16
Comprehensive	27.30
$50 Deductible Collision	46.20
Road Service/Towing	1.75
TOTAL . . . . . $	

2.

Liability (50/100/50) . . . . $	51.73
Comprehensive	26.41
Medical Payments	18.30
Uninsured Motorist	17.62
TOTAL . . . . . $	

3.

Liability (50/100/25) . . . . $	62.20
Comprehensive	37.50
Medical Payments	19.18
TOTAL . . . . . $	

4.

Liability (50/100/50) . . . . $	61.35
$100 Deductible Collision	47.51
Uninsured Motorist	21.30
Road Service/Towing	2.75
TOTAL . . . . . $	

5.

Liability (50/100/50) . . . . $	63.17
Comprehensive	27.84
Medical Payments	15.93
Uninsured Motorist	12.41
TOTAL . . . . . $	

6.

Liability (50/100/25) . . . . $	57.94
Comprehensive	36.15
Road Service/Towing	1.65
TOTAL . . . . . $	

HOSPITAL HEALTH INSURANCE
(Hospitalization)

Hospital Health Insurance pays for services and medicines you receive while you are staying in a hospital. In other words, it pays for some or all of your hospital bill. It also pays some or all of the costs for visiting an emergency room of a hospital if you have a sudden accident.

It does *not* pay any of your doctor bills, even though your doctor may be treating you while you are staying in the hospital.

NONHOSPITAL HEALTH INSURANCE

Nonhospital Health Insurance pays for some or all of your doctor's bills. It may pay for the medicines your doctor prescribes for you. It may also pay for tests and exams you have to take in a hospital as long as you are *not* actually *staying* in a hospital. That is, it will pay for some or all of your medical costs that are *not* charged to you directly by a hospital.

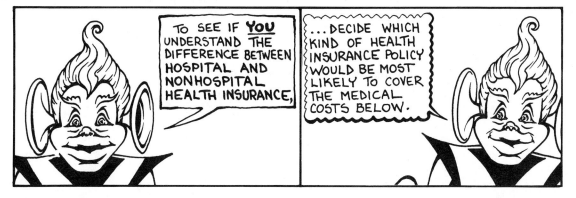

SELF-CHECK

1. A visit to your doctor's office   Hospital?   Nonhospital?

2. Treating an injury in an emergency room of a hospital.   Hospital?   Nonhospital?

3. A visit your doctor makes to you while you are a patient in the hospital   Hospital?   Nonhospital?

4. An X-ray you need while you are a patient in a hospital   Hospital?   Nonhospital?

5. A blood test taken at your doctor's office   Hospital?   Nonhospital?

SKILL: Figuring how much of a hospital bill you will have to pay when you are covered with a hospital insurance policy.

A visit to the hospital *can* be very expensive. The hospital charges you for:

(a) Rooms and meals.

(b) Tests performed in its laboratory.

(c) Services of special nurses.

(d) The use of the operating room and staff (if any).

When you leave the hospital, you'll get a bill showing the total you owe.

Look at the hospital bill below and then at the health insurance plan beside it.

BETTER-GET-BETTER HOSPITAL BILL	
Room & Meals, $105 per day	$ 525.00
Tests	68.34
Special Duty Nurse	105.00
Operating Room & Staff	355.65
TOTAL	$1,053.99

HEALTH INSURANCE PLAN
Hospital Benefits

Room & Meals.....100% payment
Tests..............60% payment
Special Duty Nurses....No Benefit
Operating Room
  & Staff...........100% payment

SAMPLE:

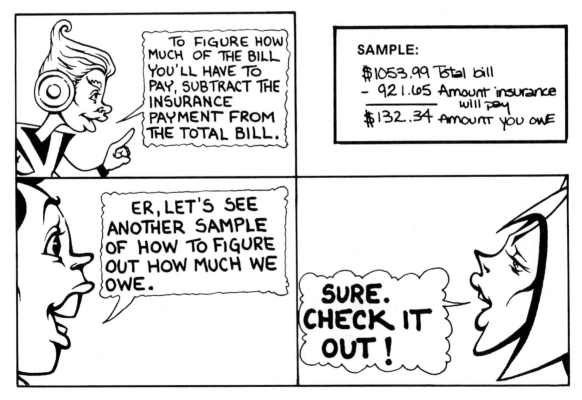

ITEM ON BILL	BENEFIT	PAYMENT
Room & Meals, $105 per day $525.00	100% payment up to $20,000	$525.00 X 1 = $525.00 → $525.00
Tests 68.34	60% payment	$68.34 X .60 = $41.00 → $41.00
Special Duty Nurse 105.00	No payment	$105 X 0 = 0 → $0
Operating Room and Staff 355.65	100% payment	$355.65 X 1 = $355.65 → $355.65
TOTAL HOSPITAL BILL $1,053.99		
TOTAL PAYMENT BY INSURANCE CO. . . . . . $ 921.65		$921.65

TO FIGURE HOW MUCH OF THE BILL YOU'LL HAVE TO PAY, SUBTRACT THE INSURANCE PAYMENT FROM THE TOTAL BILL.

SAMPLE:

$1053.99 Total bill
− 921.65 Amount insurance will pay
$132.34 Amount you owe

ER, LET'S SEE ANOTHER SAMPLE OF HOW TO FIGURE OUT HOW MUCH WE OWE.

SURE. CHECK IT OUT!

Buying Insurance

SAMPLE:

Hospital Bill		Insurance Payments
Room & Board	...........$1,500.00	75%
Tests & Medicine	..........342.16	100%
Special Duty Nurse	.........238.00	No Benefit
TOTAL HOSPITAL BILL	...$2,080.16	

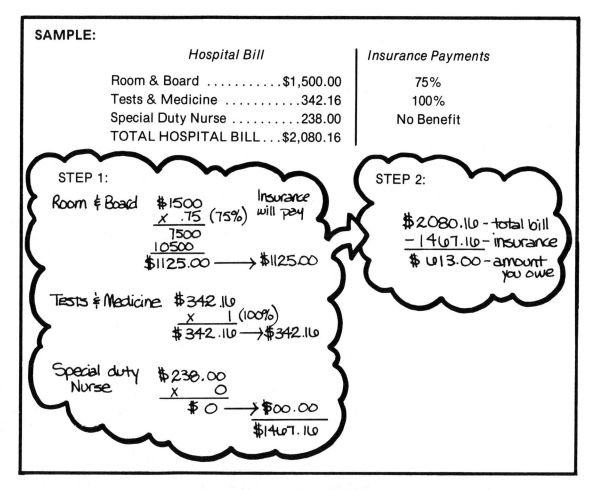

STEP 1:

Room & Board $1500
× .75 (75%)   Insurance will pay
7500
10500
$1125.00 ⟶ $1125.00

Tests & Medicine $342.16
× 1 (100%)
$342.16 ⟶ $342.16

Special duty Nurse $238.00
× 0
$0 ⟶ $00.00
$1467.16

STEP 2:

$2080.16 - total bill
- 1467.16 - insurance
$ 613.00 - amount you owe

Use the above formula to figure what you would have to pay for each of the following hospital bills. Round your answer to the nearest cent when necessary.

✓ 1.

Hospital Bill	Insurance Will Pay
Room & Board $1,530.00	85%
Tests & Medicine $ 633.50	100%
Operating Room & Staff $ 535.00	100%
TOTAL......$2,698.50	

✓ 2.

Hospital Bill	Insurance Will Pay
Room & Board $2,538.00	95%
Special Duty Nurse $ 650.00	25%
Tests & Medicine $ 238.50	100%
Operating Room & Staff $ 572.75	85%
TOTAL......$3,999.25	

3.

Hospital Bill	Insurance Will Pay
Room & Board $ 250.85	100%
Tests & Medicine $ 163.40	100%
Operating Room & Staff $ 253.25	100%
TOTAL ......$ 667.50	

4.

Hospital Bill	Insurance Will Pay
Room & Board $ 349.20	75%
Operating Room & Staff $ 153.50	85%
Special Duty Nurse $ 95.75	No Benefit
TOTAL ......$ 598.45	

5.

Hospital Bill	Insurance Will Pay
Room & Board $2,475.63	100%
Operating Room & Staff $ 555.65	95%
Tests & Medicine $ 342.50	95%
TOTAL......$3,373.78	

6.

Hospital Bill	Insurance Will Pay
Room & Board $ 748.20	95%
Operating Room & Staff $ 253.60	100%
Tests & Medicine $ 106.05	50%
TOTAL......$1,107.85	

7.

Hospital Bill	Insurance Will Pay
Room & Board $ 347.50	95%
Special Duty Nurse $ 50.75	100%
Operating Room & Staff $ 163.82	75%
TOTAL......$ 562.07	

8.

Hospital Bill	Insurance Will Pay
Room & Board $ 653.24	100%
Tests & Medicine $ 75.25	85%
Operating Room & Staff $ 563.30	85%
TOTAL......$1,291.79	

For more practice in figuring the total cost of health insurance, work the following problems.

1.

Hospital Bill	Insurance Will Pay
Room & Board $ 75.00	100%
Operating Room & Staff $ 75.00	75%
Tests & Medicine $ 15.00	75%
TOTAL $165.00	

2.

Hospital Bill	Insurance Will Pay
Room & Board $1,753.60	100%
Tests & Medicine $ 575.90	100%
TOTAL...... $2,329.50	

3.

Hospital Bill	Insurance Will Pay
Room & Board $275.85	100%
Tests & Medicine $ 53.28	90%
Operating Room & Staff $165.00	85%
TOTAL $494.13	

4.

Hospital Bill	Insurance Will Pay
Room & Board $2,746.20	95%
Tests & Medicine $ 274.90	95%
Special Duty Nurse $ 105.28	95%
TOTAL...... $3,126.38	

SKILL: Determining the monthly payments for a term life insurance policy.

One of the most popular kinds of life insurance is *term life insurance.* It is popular because it's usually the least expensive to buy. A term policy protects your for a specific period of time. When the period ends, you have to renew the policy to keep your protection. When you renew the policy, you will have to pay a higher rate.

To determine the monthly payments for a term life insurance policy, divide the yearly cost by 12. (Round to the nearest cent, when necessary.)

SAMPLE

Mr. Sanchez bought a $20,000 term life insurance policy. The policy will last for 5 years. It costs $48 per year. How much does it cost per month?

Solve each of the following problems. Round your answers to the nearest cent when necessary.

√ 1. Joan wants to buy a $15,000 term life insurance policy that will last 10 years. The policy costs $36.50 per year. How much does the policy cost her per month?

√ 2. The This'll Kill Ya Insurance Company offered a $25,000 term life insurance policy to Walter Sickly for a yearly cost of $46.78. What will Mr. Sickly's monthly payments be if he buys the policy?

3. George Krank spent a total of $200 for his $10,000 term life insurance policy—$20 per year for ten years. What were his monthly payments?

4. The Better Stay Healthy Insurance Company collected a total of $600 from one customer for a $4,000, 20-year term life insurance policy. That worked out to a yearly payment of $30. What was the customer's monthly payment?

5. A 20 year old woman buys a $7,000 term life insurance policy that will last 15 years. Her yearly payments are $35.50. What are her monthly payments?

6. Willy Fading bought a $1,000 term life insurance policy that lasted 5 years. He paid a total of $300, or $60 per year. How much did he pay per month?

7. The Eternal Life Insurance Company sold Rhonda Heavenly a $35,000 term life insurance policy. The policy was for a period of ten years. She paid $49.83 per year. How much did she pay per month?

8. Henry Mort paid a total of $2,000 for his 25-year term life insurance policy. That worked out to a payment of $80 per year. How much did he pay per month?

For more practice in figuring the cost of life insurance, solve these problems. Round your answer to the nearest cent when necessary.

1. Bill Hands bought a $10,000 term life insurance policy that will last 5 years. He pays $60 per year for it. How much does he pay per month?

2. The Random Life Insurance Company sold Wanda Keel a $5,000 term life insurance policy for a 10 year period. Wanda paid a total of $450 for the policy, or $45 per year. How much did she pay per month?

3. What are the monthly payments for a 5 year, $25,000 term life insurance policy that costs $85 per year?

4. The yearly cost of a $2,000, 5 year term life insurance policy is $37.50. What is the monthly cost?

5. The total cost of a $20,000 term life insurance policy for a 15 year period is $1,125. That works out to $75 per year. What is the monthly cost for the policy?

6. Bob Fleet pays $56 per year for a $7,500 term life insurance policy. The policy is good for 7 years. What is his monthly payment?

7. The Better-Pay-Up Insurance Company sold a customer a $50,000 term life insurance policy at a cost of $150 per year. The term of the policy is 10 years. How much did the customer have to pay for the policy per month?

8. Mortimer Herald bought a $3,000 term life insurance policy at a cost of $85.50 per year. The policy will last ten years. How much does he pay per month?

Chapter 10
Self-Test

For items 1 through 4, use the price list below to determine the total yearly cost of liability insurance. (See pages 257-260.)

Auto Insurance Price List			
Liability: 6 Month Policy			
5/10/5	$110.00	20/40/20	$134.20
10/20/10	$125.25	25/50/10	$135.50
15/30/10	$130.00	25/50/25	$137.82
15/30/15	$132.50	50/100/25	$138.00
20/40/10	$133.70	50/100/50	$142.16

1. Norton Ames, 15/30/15.

2. Rita Lopez, 20/40/20.

3. Martha Lynch, 50/100/50

4. Paula Sultan, 20/40/10.

For items 5 through 8, find the total costs of the insurance policies shown. (See pages 261-264.)

5.

Liability (50/100/25)	$62.35
Comprehensive	$26.42
Uninsured Motorist	$18.00
Medical Payments	$22.16

6.

Liability (60/100/15)	$48.12
$100 Deductible Collision	$26.50
Road Service/Towing	$ 3.00

7.

Liability (50/100/50)	$73.18
Comprehensive	$32.00
Medical Payments	$22.50
Uninsured Motorist	$18.75

8.

Liability (25/50/10)	$43.12
$50 Deductible Collision	$35.30
Comprehensive	$23.19
Uninsured Motorist	$21.50
Road Service/Towing	$ 5.75
Medical Payments	$18.00

For items 9 through 11, decide which kind of health insurance policy would be most likely to cover the medical costs described. (See pages 265-266.)

9. A blood test, taken while you are a patient in the hospital.   Hospital?   Nonhospital?

10. The treatment of an injury in the emergency room of a hospital.   Hospital?   Nonhospital?

11. A visit to the doctor's office for a routine checkup.   Hospital?   Nonhospital?

For items 12 through 15, figure how much of the total hospital bill will have to be paid by the patient. (See pages 266-271.)

12.

HOSPITAL BILL		INSURANCE PAYMENT
Room and Board	$2,100.00	75%
Tests and Medicine	418.72	75%
Special Duty Nurse	217.35	No Benefit
Total Hospital Bill	$2,736.07	

13.

HOSPITAL BILL		INSURANCE PAYMENT
Room and Board	$1,875.00	100%
Operating Room and Staff	516.50	50%
Tests and Medicine	242.00	100%
Total Hospital Bill	$2,633.50	

14.

HOSPITAL BILL		INSURANCE PAYMENT
Room and Board	$1,502.26	100%
Operating Room and Staff	650.00	80%
Tests and Medicine	341.22	100%
Special Duty Nurse	165.00	75%
Total Hospital Bill	$2,658.48	

15.

HOSPITAL BILL		INSURANCE PAYMENT
Room and Board	$3,225.80	100%
Tests and Medicine	1,326.24	85%
Total Hospital Bill	$4,552.04	

For items 16 through 18, determine the monthly payments for the term life insurance policies described. Round answers to the nearest cent when necessary. (See pages 271-274.)

16. Melissa Granger bought a $25,000 term life insurance policy. The policy will last for 6 years. It costs $50 per year. How much does it cost per month?

17. The Phillips Insurance Company sold Clive Crawford a $30,000 term life insurance policy. It was for a period of 15 years. He pays $60.00 per year. How much does he pay per month?

18. Doris Carrington wants to buy a $10,000 life insurance policy that will last 5 years. The policy costs $35.50 per year. How much will the policy cost Doris per month?

MEET THE COMPUTER

UNDERSTANDING THE BASIC PRINCIPLES OF COMPUTERS.

KEY WORDS:

1. **Arithmetic Unit:** the part of the processing unit of a computer which performs math operations with great speed.
2. **Binary Digits:** the digits of a binary number system, of which there are only two—''1'' and ''0''.
3. **Binary Place Value:** a place value system which is based on the number 2. It begins with a ones place, but each place value to the left is worth *twice* the value of the place on its right.
4. **Computer:** an electronic machine invented by man to help keep track of great amounts of information and to help solve certain kinds of problems with lightning speed.
5. **Control Unit:** the part of the processing unit of a computer which directs all the activity in the processing unit. It receives instructions from the input unit, can

give information to or retract it from the memory unit, and directs the arithmetic unit to solve certain problems.

6. **Data:** information which is put into the computer.

7. **Input Unit:** the unit of a computer which is used to put information into the computer. It also gives the computer instructions about what to do with the information it has.

8. **Memory Unit:** the part of the processing unit of a computer which stores information.

9. **Output Unit:** the unit of a computer which gives the computer a way to tell people its answers to the instructions. Usually, the output unit prints its answers very rapidly on paper.

10. **Printout:** the paper on which the output unit has printed its answers to the computer's instructions.

11. **Processing Unit:** the part of a computer which is most complex, because it has 3 smaller units within it—the memory unit, the control unit, and the arithmetic unit.

12. **Programming:** the act of putting information into the input unit of a computer.

SKILL: Understanding what a computer is and why it can be useful.

One evening the three Arithmians had a group of their human friends over for dinner. One of the humans had just started a new job with a company which made computer parts, and he asked Anja whether there had been computers on Arithmia.

Everyone wanted to know all about the computer. Anja, Miro, and Ranzo were very glad that they could help their friends, since these friends had helped them learn Earth customs. The Arithmians soon discovered that the humans had a lot of wrong ideas about what a computer is and what it can do.

Remember, a computer is just a machine. Like any machine, it has been made by man and is used by man. It cannot work without man. Man is involved with computers in all these ways:

A computer scientist designs it.

A computer engineer makes sure it is built correctly.

A computer technician helps make and assemble its parts.

A computer programmer designs the information that the computer "knows".

A computer operator puts information into the computer.

A computer printer operator makes sure the computer delivers its answers.

A COMPUTER IS PROBABLY THE MOST COMPLEX MACHINE MAN HAS EVER INVENTED.

BUT YOU CAN BEGIN TO UNDERSTAND HOW THE COMPUTER WORKS BY UNDERSTANDING ITS PARTS, OR UNITS.

THERE ARE 3 BASIC PARTS TO A COMPUTER. EACH UNIT IS ITSELF A MACHINE.

These are the three units which work together to form the system of machines which we call a computer.

COMPUTER

Input Unit

Processing Unit

Output Unit

INPUT UNIT: This unit sometimes looks like a T.V. set with a typewriter attached to it. The input unit is used to put information (called data) into the computer system. This is called *programming* a computer. The input unit is also used to give the computer instructions about what to do with the information it has.

PROCESSING UNIT: This unit is the most complex part of the computer. It is actually made up of three smaller units—the memory unit, the control unit, and the arithmetic unit.

    Memory Unit: This unit stores information. Many people compare this unit to a post office with millions of tiny mailboxes. Each of the tiny mailboxes holds data. Each mailbox has an ''address'', so the data it contains can be found quickly.

    Control Unit: This unit directs all the activity in the processing unit. It receives instructions from the input unit. These instructions may include putting information into the memory unit, or taking information out of the memory unit. The control unit can also tell the arithmetic unit to solve certain problems.

    Arithmetic Unit: The arithmetic unit can perform math operations. It can add, subtract, multiply, and divide with lightning speed.

OUTPUT UNIT: This unit provides a way for the computer to tell people the computer's answer to its instructions. Often, the output unit prints its answers very quickly on paper. This paper is called a *computer printout.*

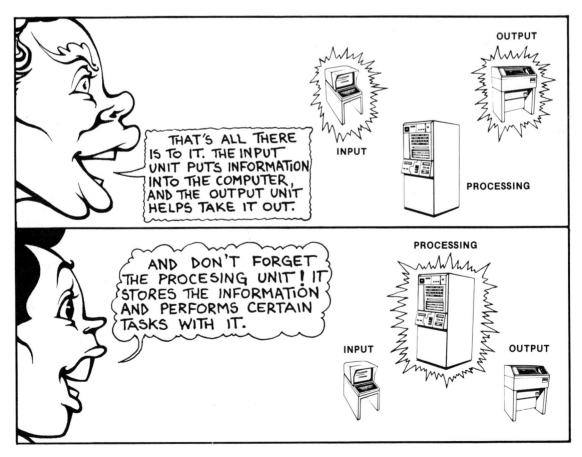

SELF-CHECK:

1. In what part of the processing unit does the computer store information?

2. Putting data into a computer is called what?

3. What part of the processing unit can add numbers?

SKILL: Understanding how a computer works with numbers (binary place value).

A computer works with numbers. Numbers are really the only thing a computer can handle. All information that goes into a computer is translated into numbers, so that the computer can do its work.

Look at this number. Can you read it? **1 1 0 0**

To most people, this number would mean *one thousand, one hundred.* Most people would write it *1,100.* We read and write the number this way because of the place value system we use in everyday life. Think about why *1100* means one thousand, one hundred to you.

Thousands Place	Hundreds Place	Tens Place	Ones Place
1	1	0	0

How many in the thousands place? ☐1 = 1000   1,100

How many in the hundreds place? ☐1 = 100   or

How many in the tens place? ☐0 = 0   one thousand

How many in the ones place? ☐0 = 0   one hundred

Math for Everyday Living   285

In everyday life, we use a number system that is based on ones, tens, hundreds, and thousands. Each place or column in a number has its own value—1, 10, 100, or 1,000. This makes no sense to a computer. A computer uses a *different* place value system.

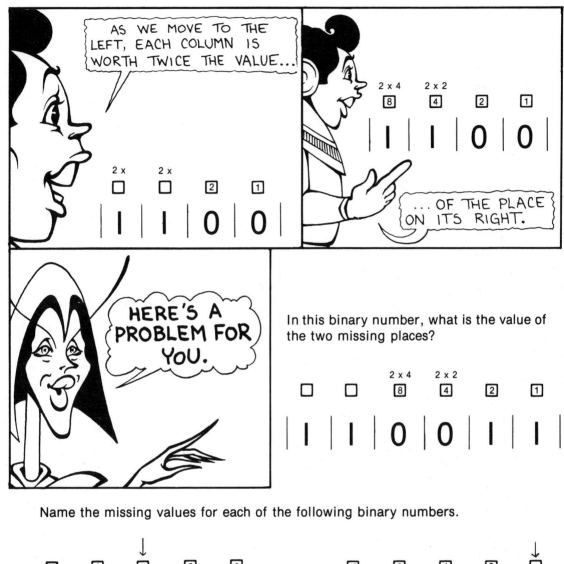

In this binary number, what is the value of the two missing places?

Name the missing values for each of the following binary numbers.

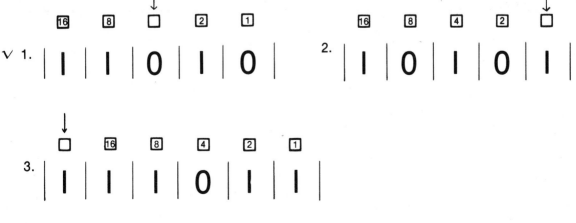

↓
□ 32 16 8 4 2 1

4. | 1 | 0 | 0 | 0 | 0 | 0 | 0 |

Now, you have seen a lot of binary numbers. Here are some more to look at closely. They are all different numbers, but in what ways are they alike?

1. **1 0 1**

2. **0 0 0 1**

3. **1 0 1 0 0**

4. **1 1 1 0 0**

5. **0 1 1 0**

6. **1 1 1 1**

Panel 1: IN OUR EVERYDAY PLACE VALUE SYSTEM, WE CAN PUT ANY DIGIT OR NUMBER FROM 0-9 IN A PLACE...

Panel 2: ...LIKE THIS!

$$974 = 9 \boxed{\text{hundreds}} = 900$$
$$7 \boxed{\text{tens}} = 70$$
$$4 \boxed{\text{ones}} = 4$$
$$974$$

Panel 3: BUT A COMPUTER USES ONLY TWO DIGITS - **1** AND **0**.

Panel 4: YES! REMEMBER THAT A BINARY NUMBER CAN NEVER LOOK LIKE THIS. [36]

Can you "count" like a computer? Translate the following binary numbers into numbers you use everyday.

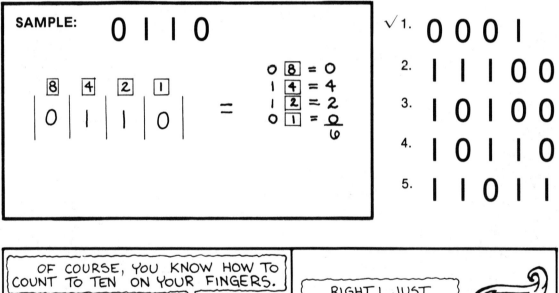

√ 1. 0 0 0 1

2. 1 1 1 0 0

3. 1 0 1 0 0

4. 1 0 1 1 0

5. 1 1 0 1 1

JUST FOR FUN

A computer uses numbers—*binary numbers*—to do its math work. It uses binary numbers to read words, too. Information that goes into a computer through its input unit—everyday numbers, letters, words—is translated into the binary numbers that the computer can understand.

To program a computer to understand the letters of the alphabet, you would have to develop a code. In this code, each letter would have a binary number which stands for it. Suppose the code looked like this:

Letter	Binary Number	Letter	Binary Number	Letter	Binary Number
A	16	J	25	S	34
B	17	K	26	T	35
C	18	L	27	U	36
D	19	M	28	V	37
E	20	N	29	W	38
F	21	O	30	X	39
G	22	P	31	Y	40
H	23	Q	32	Z	41
I	24	R	33	Space	42

Using this code, what would the message below "say" to the computer? To find out, translate each binary number into an everyday number. Then find the number in the code above and write the matching letter (or word space) in the proper place. The first binary number has been done. (Do your work on a separate piece of paper.)

10010	11110	11100	11111	100100	100011
18					
C					

10100	100001	100010	101010	10010	10000

11101	11101	11110	100011	101010	11011

10000	100100	10110	10111

SKILL: Recognizing some specific uses of computers.

292   Meet The Computer

- Banks use computers to keep constant track of money people put into and take out of their accounts.

- Utility companies use computers to figure exactly how much customers owe for the gas, electricity, and water they use.

- Airlines use computers to book flights for people anywhere in the world.

- Large stores use computers to keep track of the products they sell. Computers also help make sure that a store is always stocked with goods you want to buy.

- Your own school may use a computer to keep track of your attendance, the courses you take, and your grades.

- More and more, schools are using computers to help teach math, English, and foreign languages.

Computers are used in everyday life in many places and for many different purposes. To find out more about computers, ask your school librarian to help you find a book that will explain how and where computers are used.

SELF-CHECK:

1. Is it true that computers can think by themselves?

2. What are the basic parts of a computer?

3. How is the binary number system different from the number system we use everyday?

4. What are some specific uses of computers?

WARM-UP PROBLEMS

ADDITION

1.
```
   76
+  43
```

2.
```
   647
+  658
```

3.
```
   68
+   9
```

4.
```
    23
    64
    38
    75
+   48
```

5.
```
   378
   482
   950
   507
+  129
```

6.
```
$ 46.89
+ 37.07
```

7.
```
   26,964
+  53,629
```

8.
```
    8,264
    1,956
       87
+ 593,246
```

9. 187,403 + 56,462 + 1,007 + 850,071

10. 3,428 + 645 + 16,852 + 663,042

SUBTRACTION

1.
```
   47
-  23
```

2.
```
$ 3.25
-  2.17
```

3.
```
5,216
- 127
```

4.
```
87,767
- 3,817
```

5.
```
6,314
- 4,528
```

6.
```
28,642
- 4,803
```

7.
```
7,000
- 4,317
```

8.
```
30,208
-  679
```

9. 9,905 - 737

10. $307.76 - $143.07

MULTIPLICATION

1. 342
    x 2

2. $ 4.75
   x   3

3. 12,403
   x   7

4.   74
   x   40

5.   35
   x 84

6.   472
   x 207

7. $5.83
   x   48

8. 5,826
   x 2,007

9. 234 x 547

10. $5.07 x 38

DIVISION

1. 7) $490

2. 4) 7,250

3. 5) 10,155

4. 30) $270.00

5. 20) 889

6. 61) $49.41

7. 33) 26,466

8. 67) 3,164

9. 19) $2.66

10. 214) 11,342

ROUNDING

Round these to the nearest ten:

1. 489

2. 24,538

3. 6,981

Round these to the nearest hundred:

4. 4,527

5. 63,281

6. 6,918

7. 24,879

Round these to the nearest thousand:

8. 38,501

9. 642,399

10. 43,562

ADDING FRACTIONS

1. $\dfrac{1}{12}$
$+\dfrac{5}{12}$

2. $\dfrac{3}{8}$
$+\dfrac{3}{8}$

3. $\dfrac{1}{3}$
$+\dfrac{1}{4}$

4. $\dfrac{2}{5}$
$+\dfrac{1}{3}$

5. $8\dfrac{1}{3}$
$+6$

6. $3\dfrac{2}{5}$
$+4\dfrac{1}{5}$

7. $6\dfrac{3}{7}$
$+7\dfrac{4}{7}$

8. $4\dfrac{1}{3}$
$+2\dfrac{1}{6}$

9. $3\dfrac{1}{4}$
$+8\dfrac{1}{6}$

10. $6\dfrac{5}{8}$
$+4\dfrac{5}{6}$

SUBTRACTING FRACTIONS

1. $\dfrac{7}{8}$
$-\dfrac{3}{8}$

2. $\dfrac{5}{6}$
$-\dfrac{1}{6}$

3. $\dfrac{9}{10}$
$-\dfrac{3}{5}$

4. $\dfrac{3}{4}$
$-\dfrac{1}{2}$

5. $7\dfrac{2}{3}$
-3

6. $8\dfrac{3}{7}$
$-5\dfrac{1}{7}$

7. $9\dfrac{5}{8}$
$-2\dfrac{3}{8}$

8. $8\dfrac{7}{12}$
$-3\dfrac{1}{6}$

9. $5\dfrac{1}{5}$
$-2\dfrac{4}{5}$

10. $7\dfrac{1}{10}$
$-2\dfrac{4}{5}$

MULTIPLYING FRACTIONS

1. $\dfrac{4}{5} \times \dfrac{1}{6}$

2. $\dfrac{2}{3} \times \dfrac{6}{8}$

3. $\dfrac{12}{25} \times \dfrac{5}{18}$

4. $12 \times \dfrac{3}{4}$

5. $\dfrac{1}{2} \times 8$

6. $1\dfrac{1}{2} \times 2\dfrac{1}{3}$

7. $1\dfrac{1}{3} \times \dfrac{3}{4}$

8. $2\dfrac{3}{8} \times 3\dfrac{1}{8}$

9. $24 \times \dfrac{1}{12}$

10. $2\dfrac{7}{8} \times 3\dfrac{4}{5}$

DIVIDING FRACTIONS

1. $4 \div \frac{1}{3}$ **2.** $\frac{3}{4} \div 6$ **3.** $\frac{2}{3} \div \frac{1}{3}$ **4.** $\frac{1}{2} \div \frac{1}{6}$

5. $\frac{7}{10} \div \frac{7}{15}$ **6.** $10 \div \frac{6}{9}$ **7.** $2\frac{1}{2} \div \frac{3}{4}$ **8.** $3 \div 1\frac{1}{2}$

9. $8 \div 3\frac{1}{5}$ **10.** $12 \div 2\frac{4}{7}$

ADDING DECIMALS

1.   .7
  +   .2

2.   .36
  + .51

3.   .03
  + .09

4.   .567
  + .123

5.   .464
  + .177

6.   .386
  + .037

7.   85.4
  + 25.6

8.   8.40
  +   .59

9. $3.51 + 4.6$

10. $.486 + 5.5$

SUBTRACTING DECIMALS

1.   .68
   -.45

2.   .72
   -.38

3.   1.306
   - .253

4.   .68
   -.1

5. $7.372 - .930$ **6.** $4.9 - .2$ **7.** $.47 - .3$

8. $.437 - .2$ **9.** $7.4 - .92$ **10.** $10.2 - .83$

MULTIPLYING DECIMALS

1.   .6
   x .7
   _____

2.   .03
   x   4
   _____

3.   .0042
   x   5
   _____

4.   3.46
   x 26
   _____

5.   6.7
   x .05
   _____

6.   .006
   x 1.4
   _____

7. .4 x .385

8. 31.2 x .07

9. .3006 x .43

10. .007 x 3.41

DIVIDING DECIMALS

1. 6) .8550

2. 5) .025

3. .4) 2.84

4. .25) 12.5

5. 5.2) 2080

6. .05) 1.920

7. .12) 2.88

8. .09) .072

9. .05) 1

10. 3.1) .775

CHANGING DECIMALS TO PERCENTS

1. .56

2. .31

3. .92

4. .03

5. .10

6. .22

7. .01

8. .50

9. .17

10. .80

CHANGING PERCENTS TO DECIMALS

1. 35%

2. 14%

3. 50%

4. 44%

5. 8%

6. 10%

7. 6%

8. 8.2%

9. 69.7%

10. 4.9%

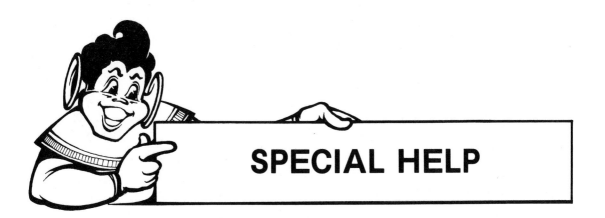

SPECIAL HELP

The charts in this section show problems which are the very basis of mathematics. Therefore, it is important for every math student to know them.

If you already know the answers to most or all of these problems, the charts may be used for review. If you do not know all the answers, you may use these tables as a reference when you are working the various problems in this book.

If necessary, have your teacher show you how to use the multiplication table for basic division problems and the addition table for basic subtraction problems.

ADDITION

1	2	3	4	5	6	7	8	9
$+\ 0$	$+\ 0$	$+\ 0$	$+\ 0$	$+\ 0$	$+\ 0$	$+\ 0$	$+\ 0$	$+\ 0$
1	2	3	4	5	6	7	8	9

1	2	3	4	5	6	7	8	9
$+\ 1$	$+\ 1$	$+\ 1$	$+\ 1$	$+\ 1$	$+\ 1$	$+\ 1$	$+\ 1$	$+\ 1$
2	3	4	5	6	7	8	9	10

1	2	3	4	5	6	7	8	9
$+\ 2$	$+\ 2$	$+\ 2$	$+\ 2$	$+\ 2$	$+\ 2$	$+\ 2$	$+\ 2$	$+\ 2$
3	4	5	6	7	8	9	10	11

1	2	3	4	5	6	7	8	9
$+\ 3$	$+\ 3$	$+\ 3$	$+\ 3$	$+\ 3$	$+\ 3$	$+\ 3$	$+\ 3$	$+\ 3$
4	5	6	7	8	9	10	11	12

1	2	3	4	5	6	7	8	9
$+\ 4$	$+\ 4$	$+\ 4$	$+\ 4$	$+\ 4$	$+\ 4$	$+\ 4$	$+\ 4$	$+\ 4$
5	6	7	8	9	10	11	12	13

1	2	3	4	5	6	7	8	9
+ 5	+ 5	+ 5	+ 5	+ 5	+ 5	+ 5	+ 5	5
6	7	8	9	10	11	12	13	14

1	2	3	4	5	6	7	8	9
+ 6	+ 6	+ 6	+ 6	+ 6	+ 6	+ 6	+ 6	+ 6
7	8	9	10	11	12	13	14	15

1	2	3	4	5	6	7	8	9
+ 7	+ 7	+ 7	+ 7	+ 7	+ 7	+ 7	+ 7	+ 7
8	9	10	11	12	13	14	15	16

1	2	3	4	5	6	7	8	9
+ 8	+ 8	+ 8	+ 8	+ 8	+ 8	+ 8	+ 8	+ 8
9	10	11	12	13	14	15	16	17

1	2	3	4	5	6	7	8	9
+ 9	+ 9	+ 9	+ 9	+ 9	+ 9	+ 9	+ 9	+ 9
10	11	12	13	14	15	16	17	18

MULTIPLICATION

1	2	3	4	5	6	7	8	9
x 0	x 0	x 0	x 0	x 0	x 0	x 0	x 0	x 0
0	0	0	0	0	0	0	0	0

1	2	3	4	5	6	7	8	9
x 1	x 1	x 1	x 1	x 1	x 1	x 1	x 1	x 1
1	2	3	4	5	6	7	8	9

1	2	3	4	5	6	7	8	9
x 2	x 2	x 2	x 2	x 2	x 2	x 2	x 2	x 2
2	4	6	8	10	12	14	16	18

1	2	3	4	5	6	7	8	9
x 3	x 3	x 3	x 3	x 3	x 3	x 3	x 3	x 3
3	6	9	12	15	18	21	24	27

Special Help

1	2	3	4	5	6	7	8	9
x 4	x 4	x 4	x 4	x 4	x 4	x 4	x 4	x 4
4	8	12	16	20	24	28	32	36

1	2	3	4	5	6	7	8	9
x 5	x 5	x 5	x 5	x 5	x 5	x 5	x 5	x 5
5	10	15	20	25	30	35	40	45

1	2	3	4	5	6	7	8	9
x 6	x 6	x 6	x 6	x 6	x 6	x 6	x 6	x 6
6	12	18	24	30	36	42	48	54

1	2	3	4	5	6	7	8	9
x 7	x 7	x 7	x 7	x 7	x 7	x 7	x 7	x 7
7	14	21	28	35	42	49	56	63

1	2	3	4	5	6	7	8	9
x 8	x 8	x 8	x 8	x 8	x 8	x 8	x 8	x 8
8	16	24	32	40	48	56	64	72

1	2	3	4	5	6	7	8	9
x 9	x 9	x 9	x 9	x 9	x 9	x 9	x 9	x 9
9	18	27	36	45	54	63	72	81

SELECTED ANSWERS

This section contains the answers to those questions in each chapter which have check marks (√) beside them. If your answers to these questions are wrong, read the explanation of how to do the problem again. Then see if you can get the right answer. If you still do not understand how to work the problem, check with your teacher before working the rest of the practice problems for that skill. You will also find the answers to the Self-Tests here.

Chapter 1
Going Shopping

Page 12:
1. $8.49
2. $7.38

Page 15:
1. 29¢
2. 37¢

Page 19:
1. $45.00

Page 23:
1. $16.36
2. $19.86

Page 26:
1. C
2. C

Self-Test, page 29:
1. C
2. D
3. A
4. C
5. D
6. 67¢
7. $2.04

Self-Test, page 30:
8. D
9. A
10. B
11. 24¢ in coins, $6.00 in bills
12. 61¢ in coins, $2.00 in bills

Self-Test, page 31:
13. 84¢ in coins, $15.00 in bills
14. 44¢ in coins, $12 in bills
15. 2¢ in coins, $7.00 in bills

Chapter 2
Having A Job

Page 41:
1. Incorrect; net pay is $104.50
2. Correct

Page 47:
1. $138.00
2. $788.00

Page 49:
1. $218.25
2. $86.25

Page 51:
1. $142.25
2. $16,850

Page 56:
1. Gross pay = $266.00

Page 57:
2. Gross pay = $399.00

Self-Test, page 61:
1. B
2. D
3. A
4. A
5. D
6. $98.57

Self-Test, page 62:
7. $301.15
8. $207.85
9. $1,077.20
10. $356.00
11. $286.00

Self-Test, page 63:
12. $250.00

Chapter 3
Fixing Things Up

Page 70:
1. 2 gallons
2. 7 gallons

Page 73:
1. 16 rolls
2. 13 rolls

Page 76:
1. 18 sq. yds.
2. 20 sq. yds.

Page 78:
1. $40.91
2. $214.92

Self-Test, page 81:
1. 400
2. 30
3. 9
4. length x width
5. unit
6. 13 rolls
7. 20 rolls
8. 21 rolls
9. 17 rolls
10. 1 gallon
11. 2 gallons
12. 1 gallon
13. 2 gallons
14. 17 sq. yds.

15. 19 sq. yds.
16. 70 sq. yds.
17. 25 sq. yds.

Self-Test, page 82:
18. $23.39
19. $130.68
20. $232.50

Chapter 4
Buy Now—Pay Later

Page 89:
1. $52.50
2. $9.01

Page 92:
1. $6,729.10
2. $24.33

Page 95:
1. 31 days
2. 28 days

Page 101:
1. $3.84
2. $7.22

Page 106:
1. $56.67
2. $38.13

Self-Test, page 107:
1. $155.00
2. $600.00
3. $164.50
4. $156.55
5. $610.00
6. $253.09
7. 26 days
8. 20 days
9. 47 days
10. $8.28

Self-Test, page 108:
11. $32.40
12. $1.01
13. $333.33
14. $47.13
15. $254.23

Chapter 5
Making Ends Meet

Page 111:
1. $228.15
2. $292.50

Page 115:
1. $76.97
2. $10.58

Page 119:
1. Total Earnings Needed = $400.50
2. Total Earnings Needed = $615.15

Page 126:
1. $196.36

Page 127:
4. $361.68

Page 131:
1. $81.44; D

Self-Test, page 135:
1. $21.79
2. $104.96
3. $41.64
4. $334.40
5. $313.70
6. $319.85
7. $664.30
8. $590.38
9. $522.38

Self-Test, page 136:
10. $359.78
11. $493.60
12. $474.90
13. $488.48
14. $485.95
15. $275.90

Chapter 6
Buying Wisely

Page 142:
1. 40¢
2. 78¢

Page 145:
1. $2.16

Page 146:
2. $3.21

Page 148:
1. $.07 per oz.

Page 151:
1. 1.6 gal. is cheaper
2. 13 oz. is cheaper

Page 154:
1. $7.17
2. $.01

Page 157:
1. $3.65
2. $3.50

Self-Test, page 159:
1. 5 lbs. at $.34 per lb.
2. No difference
3. 7 scarves at $1.57 each
4. $.15
5. $.54
6. $.48
7. $3.36
8. $7.56
9. 43¢

Self-Test, page 160:
10. $2.38
11. $3.20
12. $6.98
13. $29.25
14. $1.95
15. $4.65

Chapter 7
Using the Bank

Page 167:
1. $7.00

Page 168:
4. $8.44

Page 171:
1. Total = $203.61
Net Deposit = $203.61
2. Total = $216.32
Net Deposit = $142.48

Page 177:
1. Check should contain the following: date (use the day you are filling out the check); the name ''Sloppy Joe's Grille'' on the ''pay to the order of'' line, followed by $15.83; next line should have written on it ''fifteen and 83/100''; your signature should appear on the proper line; and the memo line should have ''hamburger''.
2. Check should contain the following: date (use day you are working on problem); the name ''Practical Appliance Company'' on the ''pay to the order of'' line, followed by $35.50; next line should have written on it ''thirty-five and 50/100''; your signature should

appear on the proper line, and the memo line should have "toothbrush/shoe polisher".

Page 182:
1. Final balance should be $1,156.71.

Page 192:
1. Subtotal = $811.38
   Total Checks Not Listed = $271.67
   Reconciled Balance = $539.71
2. Subtotal = $658.01
   Total Checks Not Listed = $221.23
   Reconciled Balance = $436.78

Self-Test, page 195:
1. $384.92
2. $384.92
3. $214.43
4. $167.20

Self-Test, page 196:
5. $6.00
6. $11.00
7. $11.32

Self-Test, page 197:
8. No. 105
9. No. 104
10. No. 103

Self-Test, page 198:
11. $170.97
12. $978.18
13. $188.50

Chapter 8
Planning A Trip

Page 204:
1. 54 miles

Page 210:
1. 16 miles per gallon
2. 9 miles per gallon

Page 214:
1. 7 hours, 15 minutes
2. 12 hours, 15 minutes

Page 216:
1. (d) fly

Page 219:
1. Total Estimate = $578

Self-Test, page 221:
1. 67 miles
2. 71 miles
3. 86 miles
4. 70 miles

Self-Test, page 222:
5. 17 miles per gallon
6. 35 miles per gallon
7. 5 hours, 30 minutes
8. 3 hours, 15 minutes
9. 2 hours, 20 minutes
10. fly
11. drive
12. $419.00

Chapter 9
Tax Time!

Page 230:
1. Tax = $.42
   Total = $7.35
2. Tax = $.96
   Total = $16.94

Page 237:
1. Line 9c = 0
   Line 11 = $12,510.60
   Line 13 = $1,761.70

Page 240:
1. $1,518
2. $2,249

Page 242:
1. Balance Due; $813.01
2. Refund; $599.51

Page 247:
1. $114.00
2. $13.00

Self-Test, page 247:
1. $.04
2. $.58
3. $1.50
4. $7.21

Self-Test, page 248:
5. $79.25
6. $12,610.45
7. $2,135.13
8. $16,662.76
9. $2,021.46

Self-Test, page 249:
10. $1,153
11. $680
12. $1,120
13. $546
14. $458
15. $1,560

Self-Test, page 250:
16. None
17. $632.33
18. $396.91
19. None
20. 0
21. 0

Self-Test, page 251:
22. $79
23. $121
24. $91
25. $71
26. $123

Chapter 10
Buying Insurance

Page 259:
1. $276.80
2. $251.50

Page 263:
1. $102.15
2. $101.84

Page 269:
1. $229.50
2. $700.31

Page 273:
1. $3.04
2. $3.90

Self-Test, page 275:
1. $265
2. $268.40
3. $284.32
4. $267.40
5. $128.93
6. $77.62
7. $146.43
8. $146.86

Self-Test, page 276:
9. Hospital
10. Hospital
11. Nonhospital
12. $847.03
13. $258.25
14. $171.25
15. $198.94

Self-Test, page 277:
16. $4.17
17. $5.00
18. $2.96

Chapter 11
Meet the Computer

Page 287:
1. 4

Page 290:
1. 1